GOD'S DESIGN® FOR

TEACHER
SUPPLEMENT

1:1
answersingenesis
Petersburg, Kentucky, USA

ANSWERS IN GENESIS **SCIENCE** BY DEBBIE & RICHARD LAWRENCE

God's Design for Life Teacher Supplement

© 2008 by Debbie & Richard Lawrence

Published by Answers in Genesis, 2800 Bullittsburg Church Rd., Petersburg KY 41080

You may contact the authors at (970) 686-5744.

ISBN: 1-60092-232-5

Cover design & layout: Diane King
Editors: Lori Jaworski, Gary Vaterlaus

The publisher and authors have made every reasonable effort to ensure that the activities recommended in this book are safe when performed as instructed but assume no responsibility for any damage caused or sustained while conducting the experiments and activities. It is the parents', guardians', and/or teachers' responsibility to supervise all recommended activities.

Printed in China.

www.answersingenesis.org   www.godsdesignscience.com

TABLE OF CONTENTS

TEACHER INTRODUCTION

WELCOME TO GOD'S DESIGN® FOR LIFE

God's Design for Life is a series that has been designed for use in teaching life science to elementary and middle school students. It is divided into three books: *The World of Plants*, *The World of Animals*, and *The Human Body*. Each book has 35 lessons including a final project that ties all of the lessons together.

In addition to the lessons, special features in each book include biographical information on interesting people as well as fun facts to make the subject more fun.

Although this is a complete curriculum, the information included here is just a beginning, so please feel free to add to each lesson as you see fit. A resource guide is included in the appendices to help you find additional information and resources. A list of supplies needed is included at the beginning of each lesson, while a master list of all supplies needed for the entire series can be found in the appendices.

Answer keys for all review questions, worksheets, quizzes, and the final exam are included here. Reproducible student worksheets and tests may be found on the supplementary CD-Rom for easy printing. Please contact Answers in Genesis if you wish to purchase a printed version of all the student materials, or go to www.AnswersBookstore.com.

If you wish to get through the *Life* series in one year, plan on covering approximately three lessons per week. The time required for each lesson varies depending on how much additional information you include, but plan on 20 minutes per lesson for beginners (grades 1–2) and 40 to 45 minutes for grades 3–8.

Quizzes may be given at the conclusion of each unit and the final exam may be given after lesson 34.

If you wish to cover the material in more depth, you may add additional information and take a longer period of time to cover all the material, or you could choose to do only one or two of the books in the series as a unit study.

WHY TEACH LIFE SCIENCE?

Maybe you hate science or you just hate teaching it. Maybe you love science but don't quite know how to teach it to your children. Maybe science just doesn't seem as important as some of those other subjects you need to teach. Maybe you need a little motivation. If any of these descriptions fits you, then please consider the following.

It is not uncommon to question the need to teach your kids hands-on science in elementary school. We could argue that the knowledge gained in science will be needed later in life in order for your children to be more productive and well-rounded adults. We could argue that teaching your children science also teaches them logical and inductive thinking and reasoning skills, which are tools they will need to be more successful. We could argue that science is a necessity in this technological world in which we live. While all of these arguments are true, not one of them is the real reason that we should teach our children science. The most important reason to teach science in elementary school is to give your children an understanding that God is our Creator, and the Bible can be trusted. Teaching science from a creation perspective is one of the best ways to reinforce your children's faith in God and to help them counter the evolutionary propaganda they face every day.

God is the Master Creator of everything. His handiwork is all around us. Our Great Creator put in place all of the laws of physics, biology, and chemistry. These laws were put here for us to see His wisdom and power. In science, we see the hand of God at work more than in any other subject. Romans 1:20 says, "For since the creation of the world His invisible attributes are clearly seen, being understood by the things that are made, even His eternal power and Godhead, so that they [men] are without excuse." We need to help our children see God as Creator of the world around them so they will be able to recognize God and follow Him.

The study of life science helps us understand the balance of nature so that we can be good stewards of our bodies, the plants, and the animals around us. It helps us appreciate the intricacies of life and the wonders of God's creation. Understanding the world of living things from a biblical point of view will prepare our children to deal with an ecology-obsessed world. It is critical to teach our children the truth of the Bible, how to evaluate the evidence, how to distinguish fact from theory and to realize that the evidence, rightly interpreted, supports biblical creation, not evolution.

It's fun to teach life science! It's interesting, too. Children have a natural curiosity about living things, so you won't have to coax them to explore the world of living creatures. You just have to direct their curiosity and reveal to them how interesting life science can be.

Finally, teaching life science is easy. It's all around us. Everywhere we go, we are surrounded by living things. You won't have to try to find strange materials for experiments or do dangerous things to learn about life.

HOW DO I TEACH SCIENCE?

In order to teach any subject, you need to understand that people learn in different ways. Most people, and children in particular, have a dominant or preferred learning style in which they absorb and retain information more easily.

If a student's dominant style is:

Auditory He needs not only to hear the information but he needs to hear himself say it. This child needs oral presentation as well as oral drill and repetition.
Visual She needs things she can see. This child responds well to flashcards, pictures, charts, models, etc.
Kinesthetic He needs active participation. This child remembers best through games, hands-on activities, experiments, and field trips.

Also, some people are more relational while others are more analytical. The relational student needs to know why this subject is important and how it will affect him personally. The analytical student, however, wants just the facts.

If you are trying to teach more than one student, you will probably have to deal with more than one learning style. Therefore, you need to present your lessons in several different ways so that each student can grasp and retain the information.

GRADES 1–2

Because *God's Design Science* books are designed to be used with students in grades 1–8, each lesson has been divided into three sections. The "Beginner" section is for students in grades 1–2. This part contains a read-aloud section explaining the material for that lesson followed by a few questions to make sure that the students understand what they just heard. We recommend that you do the hands-on activity in the blue box in the main part of the lesson to help your students see and understand the concepts.

GRADES 3–8

The second part of each lesson should be completed by all upper elementary and junior high students. This is the main part of the lesson containing a reading section, a hands-on activity that reinforces the ideas in the reading section (blue box), and a review section that provides review questions and application questions (red box).

GRADES 6–8

Finally, for middle school/junior high age students, we provide a "Challenge" section that contains more challenging material as well as additional activities and projects for older students (green box).

We have included periodic biographies to help your students appreciate the great men and women who have gone before us in the field of science.

We suggest a threefold approach to each lesson:

Introduce the topic

We give a brief description of the facts. Frequently you will want to add more information than the essentials given in this book. In addition to reading this section aloud, you may wish to do one or more of the following:

- Read a related book with your students.
- Write things down to help your visual students.
- Give some history of the subject. We provide some historical sketches to help you, but you may want to add more.
- Ask questions to get your students thinking about the subject.
- The "FUN FACT" section adds fun or interesting information.

Make observations and do experiments

- Hands-on projects are suggested for each lesson. This part of each lesson may require help from the teacher.
- Have your students perform the activity by themselves whenever possible.

Review

- The "What did we learn?" section has review questions.
- The "Taking it further" section encourages students to
    - Draw conclusions
    - Make applications of what was learned
    - Add extended information to what was covered in the lesson

By teaching all three parts of the lesson, you will be presenting the material in a way that children with any learning style can both relate to and remember.

Also, this approach relates directly to the scientific method and will help your students think more scientifically. The *scientific method* is just a way to examine a subject logically and learn from it. Briefly, the steps of the scientific method are:

1. Learn about a topic.
2. Ask a question.
3. Make a hypothesis (a good guess).
4. Design an experiment to test your hypothesis.
5. Observe the experiment and collect data.
6. Draw conclusions. (Does the data support your hypothesis?)

Note: It's okay to have a "wrong hypothesis." That's how we learn. Be sure to help your students understand why they sometimes get a different result than expected.

Our lessons will help your students begin to approach problems in a logical, scientific way.

HOW DO I TEACH CREATION VS. EVOLUTION?

We are constantly bombarded by evolutionary ideas about living things in books, movies, museums, and even commercials. These raise many questions: Did dinosaurs really live millions of years ago? Did man evolve from apes? Which came first, Adam and Eve or the cavemen? Where did living things come from in the first place? The Bible answers these questions and this book accepts the historical accuracy of the Bible as written. We believe this is the only way we can teach our children to trust that everything God says is true.

There are five common views of the origins of life and the age of the earth:

Historical biblical account	Progressive creation	Gap theory	Theistic evolution	Naturalistic evolution
Each day of creation in Genesis is a normal day of about 24 hours in length, in which God created everything that exists. The earth is only thousands of years old, as determined by the genealogies in the Bible.	The idea that God created various creatures to replace other creatures that died out over millions of years. Each of the days in Genesis represents a long period of time (day-age view) and the earth is billions of years old.	The idea that there was a long, long time between what happened in Genesis 1:1 and what happened in Genesis 1:2. During this time, the "fossil record" was supposed to have formed, and millions of years of earth history supposedly passed.	The idea that God used the process of evolution over millions of years (involving struggle and death) to bring about what we see today.	The view that there is no God and evolution of all life forms happened by purely naturalistic processes over billions of years. Ken Ham et al., *The Answers Book*, (El Cajon: Master Books, 2000), 33–76.

Any theory that tries to combine the evolutionary time frame with creation presupposes that death entered the world before Adam sinned, which contradicts what God has said in His Word. The view that the earth (and its "fossil record") is hundreds of millions of years old damages the gospel message. God's completed creation was "very good" at the end of the sixth day (Genesis 1:31). Death entered this perfect paradise *after* Adam disobeyed God's command. It was the punishment for Adam's sin (Genesis 2:16–17; 3:19; Romans 5:12–19). Thorns appeared when God cursed the ground because of Adam's sin (Genesis 3:18).

The first animal death occurred when God killed at least one animal, shedding its blood, to make clothes for Adam and Eve (Genesis 3:21). If the earth's "fossil record" (filled with death, disease, and thorns) formed over millions of years before Adam appeared (and before he sinned), then death no longer would be the penalty for sin. Death, the "last enemy" (1 Corinthians 15:26), diseases (such as cancer), and thorns would instead be part of the original creation that God labeled "very good." No, it is clear that the "fossil record" formed some time *after* Adam sinned—not many millions of years before. Most fossils were formed as a result of the worldwide Genesis Flood.

When viewed from a biblical perspective, the scientific evidence clearly supports a recent creation by God, and not naturalistic evolution and millions of years. The volume of evidence supporting the biblical creation account is substantial and cannot be adequately covered in this book. If you would like more information on this topic, please see the resource guide in the appendices. To help get you started, just a few examples of evidence supporting biblical creation are given below:

Evolutionary Myth: Humans have been around for more than one million years.

The Truth: If people have been on earth for a million years, there would be trillions of people on the earth today, even if we allowed for worst-case plagues, natural disasters, etc. The number of people on earth today is about 6.5 billion. If the population had grown at only a 0.01% rate (today's rate is over 1%) over 1 million years, there could be 10^{43} people today (that's a number with 43 zeros after it)! Repopulating the earth after the Flood would only require a population growth rate of 0.5%, half of what it is today.

John D. Morris, Ph.D., *The Young Earth* (Colorado Springs: Creation Life Publishers, 1994), 70–71. See also "Where Are All the People" at www.answersingenesis.org/creation/v23/i3/people.asp.

Evolutionary Myth: Man evolved from an ape-like creature.

The Truth: All so-called "missing links" showing human evolution from apes have been shown to be either apes, humans, or deliberate hoaxes. These links remain missing.

Duane T. Gish, Ph.D., *The Amazing Story of Creation from Science and the Bible*, (El Cajon: Institute for Creation Research, 1990), 78–83.

Evolutionary Myth: All animals evolved from lower life forms.

The Truth: While Darwin predicted that the fossil record would show numerous transitional fossils, even more than 145 years later, all we have are a handful of disputable examples. For example, there are no fossils showing something that is part way between a dinosaur and a bird. Fossils show that a snail has always been a snail; a squid has always been a squid. God created each animal to reproduce after its kind (Genesis 1:20–25).

Ibid., p. 36, 53–60. See also www.answersingenesis.org/missinglinks.

Evolutionary Myth: Dinosaurs evolved into birds.

The Truth: Flying birds have streamlined bodies, with the weight centralized for balance in flight; hollow bones for lightness, which are also part of their breathing system; powerful muscles for flight; and very sharp vision. And birds have two of the most brilliantly-designed structures in nature—their feathers and special lungs. It is impossible to believe that a reptile could make that many changes over time and still survive.

Gregory Parker et. al., *Biology: God's Living Creation*, (Pensacola: A Beka Books, 1997) 474–475.

Evolutionary Myth: Thousands of changes over millions of years resulted in the creatures we see today.

The Truth: What is now known about human and animal anatomy shows the body structures, from the cells to systems, to be infinitely more complex than was believed when Darwin published his work in 1859. Many biologists and especially microbiologists are now saying that there is no way these complex structures could have developed by natural processes.

Ibid., p. 384–385.

Since the evidence does not support their theories, evolutionists are constantly coming up with new ways to try to support what they believe. One of their ideas is called punctuated equilibrium. This theory of evolution says that rapid evolution occurred in small isolated populations, and left no evidence in the fossil record. There is no evidence for this, nor any known mechanism to cause these rapid changes. Rather, it is merely wishful thinking. We need to teach our children the difference between science and wishful thinking.

Despite the claims of many scientists, if you examine the evidence objectively, it is obvious that evolution and millions of years have not been proven. You can be confident that if you teach that what the Bible says is true, you won't go wrong. Instill in your student a confidence in the truth of the Bible in all areas. If scientific thought seems to contradict the Bible, realize that scientists often make mistakes, but God does not lie. At one time scientists believed that the earth was the center of the universe, that living things could spring from non-living things, and that blood-letting was good for the body. All of these were believed to be scientific facts but have since been disproved, but the Word of God remains true. If we use modern "science" to interpret the Bible, what will happen to our faith in God's Word when scientists change their theories yet again?

INTEGRATING THE SEVEN C'S INTO YOUR CURRICULUM

Throughout the *God's Design® for Science* series you will see icons that represent the Seven C's of History. The Seven C's is a framework in which all of history, and the future to come, can be placed. As we go through our daily routines we may not understand how the details of life connect with the truth that we find in the Bible. This is also the case for students. When discussing the importance of the Bible you may find yourself telling students that the Bible is relevant in everyday activities. But how do we help the younger generation see that? The Seven C's are intended to help.

The Seven C's can be used to develop a biblical worldview in students, young or old. Much more than entertaining stories and religious teachings, the Bible has real connections to our everyday life. It may be hard, at first, to see how many connections there are, but with practice ,the daily relevance of God's Word will come alive. Let's look at the Seven C's of History and how each can be connected to what the students are learning.

CREATION

God perfectly created the heavens, the earth, and all that is in them in six normal-length days around 6,000 years ago.

This teaching is foundational to a biblical worldview and can be put into the context of any subject. In science, the amazing design that we see in nature—whether in the veins of a leaf or the complexity of your hand—is all the handiwork of God. Virtually all of the lessons in *God's Design for Science* can be related to God's creation of the heavens and earth.

Other contexts include:

Natural laws—any discussion of a law of nature naturally leads to God's creative power.

DNA and information—the information in every living thing was created by God's supreme intelligence.

Mathematics—the laws of mathematics reflect the order of the Creator.

Biological diversity—the distinct kinds of animals that we see were created during the Creation Week, not as products of evolution.

Art—the creativity of man is demonstrated through various art forms.

History—all time scales can be compared to the biblical time scale extending back about 6,000 years.

Ecology—God has called mankind to act as stewards over His creation.

CORRUPTION

After God completed His perfect creation, Adam disobeyed God by eating the forbidden fruit. As a result, sin and death entered the world, and the world has been in decay since that time. This point is evident throughout the world that we live in. The struggle for survival in animals, the death of loved ones, and the violence all around us are all examples of the corrupting influence of sin.

Other contexts include:

Genetics—the mutations that lead to diseases, cancer, and variation within populations are the result of corruption.

Biological relationships—predators and parasites result from corruption.

History—wars and struggles between mankind, exemplified in the account of Cain and Abel, are a result of sin.

CATASTROPHE

God was grieved by the wickedness of mankind and judged this wickedness with a global Flood. The Flood covered the entire surface of the earth and killed all air-breathing creatures that were not aboard the Ark. The eight people and the animals aboard the Ark replenished the earth after God delivered them from the catastrophe.

The catastrophe described in the Bible would naturally leave behind much evidence. The studies of geology and of the biological diversity of animals on the planet are two of the most obvious applications of this event. Much of scientific understanding is based on how a scientist views the events of the Genesis Flood.

Other contexts include:

Biological diversity—all of the birds, mammals, and other air-breathing animals have populated the earth from the original kinds which left the Ark.

Geology—the layers of sedimentary rock seen in roadcuts, canyons, and other geologic features are testaments to the global Flood.

Geography—features like mountains, valleys, and plains were formed as the floodwaters receded.

Physics—rainbows are a perennial sign of God's faithfulness and His pledge to never flood the entire earth again.

Fossils—Most fossils are a result of the Flood rapidly burying plants and animals.

Plate tectonics—the rapid movement of the earth's plates likely accompanied the Flood.

Global warming/Ice Age—both of these items are likely a result of the activity of the Flood. The warming we are experiencing today has been present since the peak of the Ice Age (with variations over time).

CONFUSION

God commanded Noah and his descendants to spread across the earth. The refusal to obey this command and the building of the tower at Babel caused God to judge this sin. The common language of the people was confused and they spread across the globe as groups with a common language. All people are truly of "one blood" as descendants of Noah and, originally, Adam.

The confusion of the languages led people to scatter across the globe. As people settled in new areas, the traits they carried with them became concentrated in those populations. Traits like dark skin were beneficial in the tropics while other traits benefited populations in northern climates, and distinct people groups, not races, developed.

Other contexts include:

Genetics—the study of human DNA has shown that there is little difference in the genetic makeup of the so-called "races."

Languages—there are about seventy language groups from which all modern languages have developed.

Archaeology—the presence of common building structures, like pyramids, around the world confirms the biblical account.

Literature—recorded and oral records tell of similar events relating to the Flood and the dispersion at Babel.

CHRIST

God did not leave mankind without a way to be redeemed from its sinful state. The Law was given to Moses to show how far away man is from God's standard of perfection. Rather than the sacrifices, which only covered sins, people needed a Savior to take away their sin. This was accomplished when Jesus Christ came to earth to live a perfect life and, by that obedience, was able to be the sacrifice to satisfy God's wrath for all who believe.

The deity of Christ and the amazing plan that was set forth before the foundation of the earth is the core of Christian doctrine. The earthly life of Jesus was the fulfillment of many prophecies and confirms the truthfulness of the Bible. His miracles and presence in human form demonstrate that God is both intimately concerned with His creation and able to control it in an absolute way.

Other contexts include:

Psychology—popular secular psychology teaches of the inherent goodness of man, but Christ has lived the only perfect life. Mankind needs a Savior to redeem it from its unrighteousness.

Biology—Christ's virgin birth demonstrates God's sovereignty over nature.

Physics—turning the water into wine and the feeding of the five thousand demonstrate Christ's deity and His sovereignty over nature.

History—time is marked (in the western world) based on the birth of Christ despite current efforts to change the meaning.

Art—much art is based on the life of Christ and many of the masters are known for these depictions, whether on canvas or in music.

CROSS

Because God is perfectly just and holy, He must punish sin. The sinless life of Jesus Christ was offered as a substitutionary sacrifice for all of those who will repent and put their faith in the Savior. After His death on the Cross, He defeated death by rising on the third day and is now seated at the right hand of God.

The events surrounding the crucifixion and resurrection have a most significant place in the life of Christians. Though there is no way to scientifically prove the resurrection, there is likewise no way to prove the stories of evolutionary history. These are matters of faith founded in the truth of God's Word and His character. The eyewitness testimony of over 500 people and the written Word of God provide the basis for our belief.

Other contexts include:

Biology—the biological details of the crucifixion can be studied alongside the anatomy of the human body.

History—the use of crucifixion as a method of punishment was short-lived in historical terms and not known at the time it was prophesied.

Art—the crucifixion and resurrection have inspired many wonderful works of art.

CONSUMMATION

God, in His great mercy, has promised that He will restore the earth to its original state—a world without death, suffering, war, and disease. The corruption introduced by Adam's sin will be removed. Those who have repented and put their trust in the completed work of Christ on the Cross will experience life in this new heaven and earth. We will be able to enjoy and worship God forever in a perfect place.

This future event is a little more difficult to

connect with academic subjects. However, the hope of a life in God's presence and in the absence of sin can be inserted in discussions of human conflict, disease, suffering, and sin in general.

Other contexts include:

History—in discussions of war or human conflict the coming age offers hope.

Biology—the violent struggle for life seen in the predator-prey relationships will no longer taint the earth.

Medicine—while we struggle to find cures for diseases and alleviate the suffering of those enduring the effects of the Curse, we ultimately place our hope in the healing that will come in the eternal state.

The preceding examples are given to provide ideas for integrating the Seven C's of History into a broad range of curriculum activities. We would recommend that you give your students, and

yourself, a better understanding of the Seven C's framework by using AiG's Seven C's of History curriculum. The curriculum provides seven lessons that will establish a solid understanding of the true history, and future, of the universe. Full lesson plans, activities, and student resources are provided in the curriculum set.

We also offer bookmarks displaying the Seven C's and a wall chart. These can be used as visual cues for the students to help them recall the information and integrate new learning into its proper place in a biblical worldview.

Even if you use other curricula, you can still incorporate the Seven C's teaching into those. Using this approach will help students make firm connections between biblical events and every aspect of the world around them, and they will begin to develop a truly biblical worldview and not just add pieces of the Bible to what they learn in "the real world."

THE WORLD OF PLANTS

UNIT 1
INTRODUCTION TO LIFE SCIENCE

LESSON 1

IS IT ALIVE?

BIOLOGY IS THE STUDY OF LIVING THINGS.

SUPPLY LIST

Copy of "Is It Alive?" worksheet
Six items to display/discuss: some living, some non-living (book, pet, can, eraser, plant, etc.)

BEGINNERS

- If something is alive, what are some things that it will do? **Eat, breathe, move, grow, reproduce, etc.**
- What are the building blocks for plants and animals? **Cells.**
- Is it alive? **Answers will vary.**

WHAT DID WE LEARN?

- What are the six questions you should ask to determine if something is alive? **Does it eat?, Does it breathe?, Does it grow?, Does it reproduce?, Can it move?, Does it have cells?**

TAKING IT FURTHER

- Is a piece of wood that has been cut off of a tree living? (Hint: Is it growing? Can it respond?) **No, it is not living anymore; although the tree it came from may still be living.**
- Is paper alive? **No. It is made from wood but it is not alive.**
- Is a seed alive? **This is a harder question. A seed has the potential for life, but it is not growing. You have to decide for yourself.**

LESSON 2

WHAT IS A KINGDOM?

IT'S ALIVE, BUT WHAT IS IT?

SUPPLY LIST

Poster board   Copy of "Clue Cards"   Pen   Scissors

BEGINNERS

- Which living things can make their own food—plants or animals? **Plants.**
- Why do plants need sunshine? **They use sunlight to make food.**
- Name one important difference between plants and animals. **Accept reasonable answers.**

CLUE CARDS

- **Plants only—Chlorophyll, photosynthesis, needs sun, cannot move around, needs carbon dioxide, created on the 3rd day of creation. Animals only—Moves around, cannot make food, carbon dioxide is a waste product, no chlorophyll. Both—Alive, cells, reproduces same kind, needs oxygen, designed by God, eaten by animals.**

WHAT DID WE LEARN?

- What do plants and animals have in common? **God created them all, all are alive, all have cells, all reproduce their own kind, and all need oxygen.**
- What makes plants unique? **They have chlorophyll, perform photosynthesis, and cannot move freely.**
- What makes animals unique? **They cannot produce their own food and can move freely.**

TAKING IT FURTHER

- Are mushrooms plants? **No, they do not have chlorophyll or perform photosynthesis.**
- Why do you think they are or are not? **Fungi have most of the characteristics of plants, but do not have chlorophyll and can live without sunlight. This is why scientists now group them in their own kingdom.**

LESSON 3

CLASSIFICATION SYSTEM

TAXONOMY—CLASSIFICATION OF LIVING THINGS

SUPPLY LIST

Plant and animal guides or an encyclopedia

BEGINNERS

- How do scientists split living things into groups? **They examine what is the same and what is different and put things that are similar in the same group.**
- What is the first major division of living things called? **A kingdom.**
- What are the two main groups of animals? **Those with backbones and those without backbones.**

WHAT DID WE LEARN?

What are the five kingdoms recognized today? **Plants, animals, fungi, protists, and monerans.**
- How do scientists determine how to classify a living thing? **They look at common characteristics and at different characteristics.**
- What are the seven levels of the classification system? **Kingdom, phylum, class, order, family, genus, and species.**

TAKING IT FURTHER

- Why can pet dogs breed with wild wolves? **They are both the same kind of animal. Wolves, jackals, coyotes, wild dogs, and domestic dogs all came from the same ancestors. If any two animals can produce fertile offspring then they are most likely from the same animal kind. Wolves don't generally breed with domestic dogs because of their location and habits, but biologically they are the same kind of animal.**

- How many of each animal did Noah take on the Ark? **Two of some animals and seven of other animals (see Genesis 7). Noah would only have taken two canines (dogs) on the Ark. Afterwards, the offspring of those two dogs resulted in the wide variety of dogs we see today.**

CHALLENGE: PLANT CLASSIFICATION

Note: The third paragraph of the Challenge section should be replaced with this one.

Nonvascular plants are divided into three groups: mosses, liverworts, and hornworts. Together these are called bryophytes. These nonvascular plants have leaves and stems, but do not have true roots. They reproduce by spores, not with flowers. The bryophytes tend to grow in clumps in moist areas. You may find them growing on tree trunks or along streams, but don't confuse them with the algae growing in the water. Even though algae contain chlorophyll, they are not plants since they do not have leaves, stems, and roots.

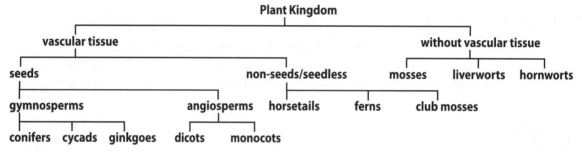

LESSON 4

PLANT & ANIMAL CELLS

THE SMALLEST UNIT OF LIFE

SUPPLY LIST

Option A: Paper models

    Colored construction paper   Scissors   Glue

Option B: 3-D models (messier but more fun)

    For each child: Small shoe box   1 qt. plastic zipper bag   Several green grapes   Several raisins 1 large red grape or marble   For everyone to use: Yellow gelatin mix (Note: mix this gelatin according to the package directions about an hour before you plan to do the project.)

Supplies for Challeng: Microscope   Slides   Onion   Sharp knife

BEGINNERS

- What shape are most animal cells? **Round.**
- What shape are most plant cells? **Rectangular.**

- What is the job of the cell membrane? **It is like skin and holds the cell together.**
- What is the job of the nucleus? **It is the brain—it tells everything else what to do.**
- What can plant cells do that animal cells cannot do? **They turn sunlight into food.**

What did we learn?
- What parts or structures do all plant and animal cells have? **Cell membrane, nucleus, vacuoles, mitochondria, and cytoplasm.**
- What structures are unique to plants? **Cell wall and chloroplasts.**
- What distinguishes animal cells from plant cells? Possible answers: **Plant cells can perform photosynthesis and have cell walls but animal cells do not; their shape is different.**

Taking it further
- A euglena is a single-celled living organism that can move around by itself. It eats other creatures, but it also has chlorophyll in its cell. Is it a plant, an animal, or something else? **Scientists do not agree on this and other unusual creatures. They usually put them in their own category, called protists.**

QUIZ 1 — Introduction to Life Science
Lessons 1–4

Mark each statement as either True or False.

1. _T_ All living creatures have cells.
2. _F_ Plants do not need oxygen.
3. _T_ Growth and change can be signs of life.
4. _F_ Non-living things absorb nutrients.
5. _F_ Plants cannot move so they are not alive.
6. _T_ A kingdom is a way to group things together by similar characteristics.
7. _F_ Plants and protists are the two main kingdoms of living things.
8. _F_ Plants and animals both have chlorophyll.
9. _T_ Vacuoles store food inside of cells.
10. _T_ The nucleus is the control center of a cell.

Short answer:

11. Name three differences between plant and animal cells: **Shape of the cells—plant cells are usually rectangular, animal cells are usually round; plant cells have chlorophyll, animal cells do not; plant cells have a cell wall, animal cells do not; only plant cells perform photosynthesis.**

12. Describe how to tell if something is alive: **Eats, breathes, grows, reproduces, moves/responds to its environment, and has cells.**

Challenge questions

Fill in the blanks using the terms below. Not all words are used.

13. The Law of **_biogenesis_** states that life always comes from life.

14. _**Chemical evolution** _ says that life originally came from non-living chemicals.

15. During _**mitosis**_ a cell divides into two identical cells.

16. A _**conifer or gymnosperm**_ is a type of plant that produces seeds in cones.

17. A _**Ginkgo**_ tree is sometimes called a living fossil.

18. _**Angiosperms**_ produce seeds that are enclosed in fruit.

19. The belief that life springs up from its environment is called _**spontaneous generation**_.

20. During _**metaphase**_ the chromosomes in a cell line up in the middle.

21. During _**anaphase**_ the duplicate chromosomes are pulled apart.

22. _**Cytokinesis**_ occurs when the cytoplasm in a cell is divided.

23. A _**dicot**_ has a seed with two parts.

24. A _**monocot**_ has a seed with only one part.

25. A cycad is a type of _**gymnosperm**_.

UNIT 2
FLOWERING PLANTS & SEEDS

LESSON 5

FLOWERING PLANTS

GOD'S GIFT OF LIFE TO THE WORLD

SUPPLY LIST

A field guide for flowers   Access to several flowering plants (What you have growing in your garden or yard is probably sufficient.)

Supplies for Challenge: Research materials—depends on your selected topic

BEGINNERS

- What are the four parts of plants? **Roots, stems, leaves, and flowers.**
- What is the job of each of the parts? **Roots hold the plant in place and suck up water and nutrients. Stems help the plant stand up and to move water and nutrients inside the plant. Leaves turn sunlight into food. Flowers produce seeds.**

WHAT DID WE LEARN?

- What are the four major parts of a plant? **Roots, stem, leaves and flowers.**
- What is the purpose for each part? **Roots hold the plant in place and suck up water and nutrients. Stems help the plant stand up and to move water and nutrients inside the plant. Leaves turn sunlight into food. Flowers produce seeds.**

TAKING IT FURTHER

- What characteristics other than the flowers can be used to help identify a plant? **Leaves, fruit, and bark can all be used to identify a plant that is not in bloom.**
- What similarities did you notice between the flowers you examined? **Answers will vary.**
- What differences did you see? **Answers will vary.**
- Can you use size to determine what a plant is? Why or why not? (Hint: Is a tiny seedling just as much an oak tree as the giant oak that is 100 years old?) **Size alone cannot tell you what a plant is.**
- Why might you need to identify a plant? Possible answers: **To recognize poisonous plants such as poison ivy, to choose good plants for a garden or landscape, and to enjoy God's creation are just a few reasons.**

LESSON 6

GRASSES

DO I HAVE TO CUT IT AGAIN, MOM?

SUPPLY LIST

Magnifying glass   Grass plant

Supplies for Challenge: Kentucky bluegrass seeds   Corn seeds   Other grass seeds as available (wheat, oats, rye, fescue, etc.)   Baking dish   Potting soil   Craft sticks   Marker
Copy of "Grass Comparison" worksheet

BEGINNERS

- Why are different types of grass so important? **They provide food for people and animals.**
- Name one kind of grass eaten by animals. **Prairie grass, hay, timothy, corn.**
- Name one kind of grass eaten by people. **Wheat, oats, rice, and corn.**

WHAT DID WE LEARN?

- Name four types of grass. **Turf, cereal, forage, and ornamental.**
- Describe the roots of a grass plant. **Fibrous root system with many small roots going out in several directions.**
- Why are grasses so important? **They are a major food source for animals and humans.**

TAKING IT FURTHER

- Why can grass be cut over and over and still grow, while a tree that is cut down will die? **Recall that the leaves of the grass grow from the base of the plant. So cutting off the top of the leaves does not damage the growing center of the plant. However, trees grow at the ends of the stems and branches.**
- Why is grass so hard to get rid of in a flower garden? **Consider the root structure; its fibrous design helps the plant spread and survive.**
- What part of grass plants do humans eat? **They generally eat the seeds.**
- What part of grass plants do most animals eat? **They usually eat the leaves and the seeds.**
- Why can a cow eat certain grasses that you can't? **Cows have a very different digestive system that can break down the grass that humans can't digest.**

LESSON 7

TREES

DID GEORGE WASHINGTON REALLY CHOP DOWN THE CHERRY TREE?

SUPPLY LIST

Index cards labeled with vocabulary words   Markers or crayons

Supplies for Challenge: Drawing materials

BEGINNERS

- What are the two different groups of trees? **Deciduous and evergreen.**
- What kind of leaves do deciduous trees have? **Flat leaves.**
- What kind of leaves do evergreen trees have? **Needles.**
- What covers a tree trunk to help protect it? **Bark.**
- How can you tell how old a tree is? **By counting its growth rings.**

WHAT KIND OF TREE IS THIS?

- **Angiosperm, broad leaf, flowers, oak, maple, cherry should all have deciduous picture only. Gymnosperm, needles, cones, fir, pine, spruce, conifer should all have evergreen only. Seeds, bark growth rings should have both pictures.**

WHAT DID WE LEARN?

- What makes a plant a tree? **A single woody stem, grows to be tall, needs no support, and has bark.**
- What are some of the differences between deciduous and evergreen trees? **Deciduous trees have broad leaves (which they lose in the winter)., flowers, and many have edible fruit. Evergreen trees have narrow leaves called needles (which they do not lose), and they have cones instead of flowers.**

TAKING IT FURTHER

- Do evergreen trees have growth rings? **Even though evergreens do not lose their leaves, they take a break from growing in the winter so they do have growth rings.**
- How long do you think a tree lives? **Some trees only live a few years and some trees live to be hundreds, or even thousands, of years old. It depends on the variety of the tree and the growing conditions.**

SEEDS

GERMINATION—THE BEGINNING OF LIFE

SUPPLY LIST

Copy of "Germination Data Sheet"   5 jars (1 with a lid)   Paper towels   Steel wool
15–20 dried bean seeds   Black construction paper   Tape

BEGINNERS

- What part of a plant grows into a new plant? **Seeds.**
- What three things must be present before a seed will start growing? **Water, warmth, and air/oxygen.**

WHAT DID WE LEARN?

- What conditions must be present for most seeds to sprout or germinate? **Water, oxygen, and warmth.**
- Is soil necessary for seeds to germinate? **No, you germinated them in wet paper towels.**

TAKING IT FURTHER

- If plants don't need soil to germinate, why do plants need soil to grow? **The seed has some stored energy that helps it get started. Once this energy is used up, the plant's roots must absorb nutrients from the soil, and the leaves will make food from the sun.**

- Our seeds germinated in the dark. Can the plants continue to grow in the dark? **No, once the seed's energy is used up, the plant needs sunlight to make more food.**

- Why do seeds require these three conditions to begin growing? **God designed them that way so that the seeds will wait until it is likely the plants will survive before they germinate. If seeds germinated in the cold, the plant may not survive because the roots would freeze. If seeds germinated without oxygen, the plant would not be able to grow and it would die. If seeds germinated without water, the plants would soon wither. If seeds continued to germinate in unfavorable conditions, many plants could become extinct.**

- How long can seeds remain dormant? **Some seeds have sprouted after 100 years or more of waiting for the right conditions.**

LESSON 9
MONOCOTS & DICOTS

WHAT'S INSIDE THAT SEED?

SUPPLY LIST

Several bean seeds (pinto, kidney, etc.) *** Soak these seeds in water for approx. 24 hours prior to use.
Several corn seeds (not popcorn) *** Soak these seeds in water for approx. 24 hours prior to use.
Dissecting scalpel or very sharp knife (for adult use only)   Magnifying glass   Jar or plastic cup
Paper towels

Supplies for Challenge: Other seeds for dissection

BEGINNERS

- Why can a seed grow for a little while when it is not planted in the soil? **The seed contains food that helps the new plant grow for a while.**

- What is on the outside of a seed? **The seed covering or seed coat that protects it.**

- How many pieces does a bean seed have? **Two.**

- How many pieces does a corn seed have? **One.**

WHAT DID WE LEARN?

- What differences did you observe between the monocot and dicot seeds? **Monocots have one part and a tougher seed coat. Dicots have two parts and a softer seed coat.**

- What parts of each seed were you able to identify? **You should have been able to identify the seed coat, hilum, plumule, radicle, cotyledons and the endosperm of the corn seed.**

- What is the plumule? **Part that grows into the stem and leaves of the plant.**

- What is the radicle? **Part that grows into the roots of the plant.**

- What is the purpose of the cotyledon? **It provides energy for the new plant until the roots get big enough to begin supporting the plant, and sometimes becomes the first embryonic leaves of a seedling.**

TAKING IT FURTHER

- Why did you need to soak the seeds before dissecting them? **Moisture is needed to soften the seed coat and begin the germination process. This is one of God's ways of preserving the seed until conditions are good for the plant to grow. If seeds sprouted when there was no water available, the young plants would soon wither and die.**

- What differences do you think you might find in plants that grow from monocot and dicot seeds? **There are differences in the root structures, stems, leaves, and flowers. We will discuss some of these in later lessons.**

CHALLENGE: GERMINATION

- **Beans—epigeal germination, Corn—hypogeal germination.**

LESSON 10

SEEDS—WHERE ARE THEY?

HOW DO THEY GET AROUND?

SUPPLY LIST

Several different fruits and vegetables (apple, tomato, peach, etc.)   Baking dish lined with aluminum foil
Several pinecones with scales tightly shut   Copy of "Seeds Get Around" worksheet

Supplies for Challenge: Several different kinds of seeds   Whole coconut or coconut seed, if available
Copy of "Water Dispersal Test"

BEGINNERS

- Name three places you can find seeds. **Fruit, vegetables, pinecones, and dead flowers.**
- Name three ways that seeds get from the plant to another location. **Carried by an animal, blown by the wind, and exploding from the seed pod.**

SEEDS GET AROUND WORKSHEET

- **Ideas might include: Wind: dandelion—parachute, maple—helicopter, Animal: cocklebur—Velcro, Explosion: touch-me-not, violets, witch hazel—bomb.**

WHAT DID WE LEARN?

- What are three ways seeds can be moved or dispersed? **By the wind, by animals or by explosion.**
- Where are good places to look for seeds? **In fruit, pinecones, or "dead" flowers.**

TAKING IT FURTHER

- How do people aid in the dispersal of seeds? Possible answers: **Farming, gardening, hiking (on our clothes), etc.**
- What has man done to change or improve seeds or plants? Possible answers: **Man has used cross-pollination and genetic alteration of seeds to develop plants that are more resistant to disease or insects, that are higher in nutritional content, have larger blossoms or have different colors, as well as many other changes.**
- If a seed is small, will the mature plant also be small? **Not usually; plants often grow large, even if they start from a small seed.**

- Do the largest plants always have the largest seeds? **No.**
- Why do you think God created many large plants to have small seeds? **Small seeds are more easily dispersed.**
- Can you name a plant that disperses its seeds by the whole plant blowing around? **Tumbleweed.**

CHALLENGE: WATER DISPERSAL

- **Plants that are close together compete for room, nutrients, water, and sunlight. Seed dispersal allows plants to spread out. This gives the seeds a better chance to land in areas where there is more room, nutrients, water, and sunlight, thus allowing new plants a better chance of survival. The coconut can float because it is less dense than water, just like a ship.**

QUIZ 2

FLOWERING PLANTS & SEEDS

LESSONS 5–10

Match the term with its definition.

1. _A_ Monocot
2. _D_ Dicot
3. _B_ Cotyledon
4. _F_ Hilum
5. _I_ Plumule
6. _G_ Radicle
7. _C_ Seed Coat
8. _E_ Deciduous
9. _H_ Evergreen

Answer yes or no. Would a seed geminate if placed in each of the following conditions? If no, explain what is missing.

10. A seed planted in a garden in the spring time and watered every day. **Yes—All necessary conditions are present.**
11. A seed in a desert. **Probably not—There is probably not enough water.**
12. A seed planted in the dirt on the moon. **No—There is not enough oxygen, moisture, or heat on the moon.**
13. A seed in an envelope at the store. **No—There is not enough moisture in the envelope.**
14. A seed in a moist paper towel in a sunny window. **Yes—All necessary conditions are present.**

Short answer:

15. Name the four organs of a plant: **Roots, Stem, Leaves, Flowers.**

CHALLENGE QUESTIONS

Mark each statement as either True or False.

16. _T_ Many plants can be used to make medicines.
17. _F_ All grass is alike.

18. _T_ Rye, wheat, and oats are all grasses.

19. _T_ Many trees have distinctive crowns.

20. _T_ A pine tree has a triangular growth habit.

21. _F_ Pruning will not affect a tree's growth habit.

22. _F_ External seed dormancy depends on temperature.

23. _T_ Some commercial growers use sulfuric acid to scarify seeds.

24. _T_ Stratification of seeds can occur in a refrigerator.

25. _F_ Seeds with double dormancy can experience scarification and stratification in either order and still germinate.

26 _F_ You will see cotyledons above ground if a plant experiences hypogeal germination.

27. _T_ Seeds absorb up to 200% more water when they germinate than they had before germination.

28. _F_ Seed dispersal is unimportant.

29. _T_ A deer can be a dispersing agent.

30. _F_ Only tiny seeds can float for water dispersal.

ROOTS & STEMS

LESSON 11

ROOTS

A GREAT FOUNDATION

SUPPLY LIST

Unpeeled carrot and any other roots you would like to examine   Magnifying glass

Jars with beans and corn from lessons 8 and 9

Supplies for Challenge: Radish seeds   Paper towels   Magnifying glass

BEGINNERS

- What are the four parts of plants? **Roots, stems, leaves, and flowers.**

- What are the two main jobs of the roots? **To hold the plant in place and to suck up water and nutrients for the plant.**

- What are the two different kinds of roots? **Taproots and fibrous roots.**

WHAT DID WE LEARN?

- What are the four organs of a plant? **Roots, stem, leaves, and flowers.**

- What are the jobs that the roots perform? **Anchoring the plant, absorbing water and nutrients, and storing extra food.**

- How can you tell what kind of root system a plant has? **You can examine the roots. Also, look at the seeds to see how many cotyledons they have. Generally, monocots have fibrous roots and dicots have taproots. We will see in future lessons that monocots and dicots usually have different types of leaves, too. This can also give us a clue to what type of root structure a plant has.**

TAKING IT FURTHER

- What kind of plants might you want to plant on a hillside? Why? **You might want to plant grass because the fibrous root system will spread out and hold the soil in place. Plants with taproots would not help stop the soil from washing away as well as plants with fibrous roots.**

- Why are the roots of plants like carrots and beets good to eat? **The leaves produce more energy than the plant can use at one time so the extra energy is converted and stored in the roots. We can eat those roots and get that energy for our bodies.**

LESSON 12

SPECIAL ROOTS

NOT ALWAYS UNDERGROUND

SUPPLY LIST

Onion with roots   Flower bulbs (tulips, daffodils, etc.), if available

Supplies for Challenge: Poster board   Pictures of special roots   Drawing materials

BEGINNERS

- How do the roots on tulip bulbs look? **Like little hairs growing out from the bottom.**
- How do plants that do not grow in soil get water? **They have special roots that can take water out of the air.**
- What special kind of roots does a mangrove tree have? **Prop roots.**

WHAT DID WE LEARN?

- What are adventitious roots? **Roots that grow individually from the stem or bulb.**
- What are aerial roots? **Roots that grow in the air.**
- What are prop roots? **Roots that grow outward from the side of the stem, then downward to provide additional support.**

TAKING IT FURTHER

- Why do you think that some plants have specialized roots? **Not all environments are equally friendly to plant growth. God designed plants to grow in many areas that are hostile to most plants.**
- Why do some plants need prop roots? **Plants that grow in very soft or often wet soil may not be anchored well enough with a single root system. They need prop roots to give additional support.**

LESSON 13

STEMS

CONNECTING IT ALL TOGETHER

SUPPLY LIST

Stalk of celery with leaves   Glass of water   Food color (red or blue)

2 clear plastic cups with potting soil   Jars with beans and corn from lessons 8 and 9

BEGINNERS

- What is the main job of the stem? **To transport water and food.**
- How are tree stems different from wildflower stems? **They are stiff and woody and covered with bark instead of being bendable.**
- How does the water and food move through the stem? **Through a series of special tubes.**

WHAT DID WE LEARN?

- What are the main functions of a stem? **To support the plant, to carry nutrients and water between the roots and the leaves and flowers, to carry food from the leaves to the rest of the plant.**

- What do we call the stem of a tree? **A trunk or a branch.**

TAKING IT FURTHER

- If a branch is 3 feet above the ground on a certain day, how far up will the branch be 10 years later? **It will still be 3 feet above the ground. The tree will get taller but the growth is as the top of the tree and the ends of the branches, so the base of that particular branch remains in the same location.**

- What are some stems that are good to eat? **Celery is a good stem. Potatoes are special stems called tubers. Onions are special stems called bulbs. These are a few examples of stems that are good to eat.**

LESSON
14

STEM STRUCTURE

HOW THEY ARE PUT TOGETHER

SUPPLY LIST

Drawing materials   Plant with new growth, if available

BEGINNERS

- Branches are what part of a plant? **The stem.**
- Name two things, besides branches, that grow from the stem. **Leaves and flowers.**

WHAT DID WE LEARN?

- What are the major structures of a stem? **Shoot, terminal bud, lateral bud, node, and internode.**
- Where does new growth occur on a stem? **Most of the growth occurs at the terminal bud. New shoots, leaves, and flowers grow at lateral buds.**
- What gives the plant its size and shape? **The collection and arrangement of stems.**

TAKING IT FURTHER

- What will happen to a plant if its terminal buds are removed? **It will stop growing. It may form new terminal buds on new shoots, but the existing stems will be unable to grow.**
- How are stems different between trees and bushes? **Trees have one main stem or trunk with many smaller stems branching off. Bushes have many stems that all grow from the roots.**
- In your experience, do flower stems have the same structures, including terminal buds, nodes, etc., as bush and tree stems? **Most plants have the same structures you learned about here. Sometimes the stems are very short and it may be difficult to identify all of the structures, but most of flowering plants have the same stem structures.**

STEM GROWTH

FURTHER UP AND FURTHER OUT

SUPPLY LIST (none)

BEGINNERS

- Why do tree trunks get bigger around every year? **New cells are formed inside the trunk and they push out on the bark.**
- When are new cells formed inside the trunk? **Mostly during the spring and summer.**
- What are growth rings? **Light and dark colored rings formed from new cells inside the trunk during growing and resting periods.**

WHAT DID WE LEARN?

- What are epidermis cells? **The cells on the outside of a young stem.**
- What is bark? **The epidermis cells that have been pushed outward, hardened, and died.**
- Name three types of cells inside a stem. **Xylem, phloem, and cambium cells.**

TAKING IT FURTHER

- Can we tell a tree's age from the rings inside the trunk? Why or why not? **Different cells are produced during different parts of the growing season, and few cells are produced during the winter so each year one set of colored bands is produced inside the trunk or stem of the tree. However, under certain conditions, multiple rings can form in a single year.**
- If you wanted to make a very strong wooden spoon, which part of the tree would you use? **The center, where the heartwood is.**
- Why don't herbaceous plants have bark? **They die at the end of each growing season so there is no time for bark to develop.**

CHALLENGE: VASCULAR TISSUE

- In lesson 13, you watched fluids moving up the stem of a stalk of celery. Do you remember how the xylem were arranged in the celery? They were arranged in a circular pattern. Would that indicate that celery is a monocot or a dicot? **Celery is a dicot.**

ROOTS & STEMS

LESSONS 11–15

Choose the best answer for each statement or question.

1. _**B**_ Which is not a function of the roots of a plant?
2. _**A**_ Which is not considered a plant organ?

3. _C_ A plant with this type of roots is most likely to live where it is dry.

4. _D_ A plant with this type of roots is most likely to live in a tree.

5. _A_ You would be most successful planting plants with these roots on a steep hill.

6. _B_ A plant with these kind of roots will be more successful in a very wet area.

7. _A_ Which is not a function of the stem?

8. _C_ What causes water to move upward in a plant?

9. _D_ What is a new stem called?

10. _C_ Where do leaves connect to the stem?

11. _B_ Which kind of cells are not found inside a stem?

12. _A_ Which cells carry water up a stem?

13. _C_ Which cells carry food down a stem?

14. _B_ Which cells protect a young stem?

15. _D_ Which cells protect mature stems?

CHALLENGE QUESTIONS

Choose the best answer for each statement or question.

16. _B_ How does primary growth change the root?

17. _A_ Where does primary growth occur in a root?

18. _B_ How is osmosis different from diffusion?

19. _D_ What role does capillarity play in plants?

20. _C_ Which type of branching results in a wide low tree or shrub?

21. _A_ How are vascular bundles arranged in an herbaceous monocot stem?

22. _D_ What type of cells produce new xylem and phloem?

UNIT 4
LEAVES

LESSON 16

PHOTOSYNTHESIS

MAKING FOOD FOR THE WORLD

SUPPLY LIST

3 mint plants or other fast-growing plants   Copy of "Photosynthesis Data Sheet"   Scissors
2 cardboard boxes that are big enough to cover a plant and allow for growth   Liquid measuring cup
Supplies for Challenge: Copy of "Photosynthesis Building Blocks" worksheet   Scissors   Tape

BEGINNERS

- What color is chlorophyll? **Green.**

- What is photosynthesis? **It is the process in which leaves turn water, carbon dioxide, and light into sugar and oxygen. It is the way plants make food.**

- What do plants produce that helps animals breathe? **Oxygen.**

WHAT DID WE LEARN?

- What are the "ingredients" needed for photosynthesis? **Water, carbon dioxide, chlorophyll, and sunlight.**

- What are the "products" of photosynthesis? **Food for the plant in the form of sugar and oxygen.**

- How did God specifically design plants to be a source of food? **Plants make their own food using the energy from the sun. They produce more than they need so the extra food energy is passed on to the animal or human that eats it.**

- How does carbon dioxide enter a leaf? **Through holes in the leaf called stomata.**

TAKING IT FURTHER

- On which day of creation did God create plants? **Day 3—Genesis 1:9–13.**

- On which day did He create the sun? **Day 4—Genesis 1:14–19.**

- Some people try to combine the Bible and evolution by saying that there were long periods of time between each day of creation. If this were true, what would have happened to all the green plants if there were a very long period of time between Day 3 and Day 4? **They all would have died.**

- In our experiment, we found that the plant that got less sunlight grew more slowly than the one that had full sunlight. Is this true for all plants? **No, many plants prefer the shade to full sun. God designed these plants to grow where other plants do not. Consider repeating this experiment with a shade-loving plant such as impatiens.**

ARRANGEMENT OF LEAVES

MAXIMIZING SUNLIGHT

SUPPLY LIST

Drawing paper   Crayons, markers, or colored pencils
Supplies for Challenge: Aloe plant or other succulent, if available

BEGINNERS

- Explain different ways that leaves can grow from stems. **Answers will vary.**
- What is the main job of the leaves? **To perform photosynthesis/make food for the plant.**
- Why are leaves arranged in different ways? **To allow the sun to shine on them most of the day.**

WHAT DID WE LEARN?

- What are four common ways leaves can be arranged on a plant? **Opposite, alternate, whorled, and rosette.**
- Why do you think God created each of these different leaf arrangements? **Each of the leaf arrangements helps to ensure that one leaf does not block the light from reaching another leaf. The different arrangements are efficient for the size and shape of the leaves.**
- Why is it important for sunlight to reach each leaf? **Leaves need sunlight for photosynthesis. This is what keeps the plant alive and growing.**

TAKING IT FURTHER

- How does efficient leaf arrangement show God's provision or care for us? **Maximizing food production in plants provides more food for all animals, as well as for humans.**
- What other feature, besides leaf arrangement, aids leaves in obtaining maximum exposure to sunlight? **Leaves turn to follow the sun. Cells away from the sun become longer than those on the sunny side, allowing the leaf to turn toward the sun as it moves through the sky.**

LEAVES—SHAPE & DESIGN

WHAT'S YOUR SHAPE?

SUPPLY LIST

1 or more large leaves freshly picked from a tree   Knife or scissors   Paper and colored pencils
Red food coloring   Bean and corn plants from lessons 8 and 9   Grass

BEGINNERS

- What shape of leaves do most plants have? **Broad leaves—wide and flat.**
- What shape are grass leaves? **Long, thin/narrow, and flat.**

- How do food and water move in leaves? **Through veins.**
- What do veins look like in grass? **Long, parallel lines.**
- What do veins look like in broad leaves? **One main vein with smaller veins branching off.**

OBSERVING LEAF SHAPES AND VEIN ARRANGEMENTS

- How are their shapes and vein arrangements different? **Corn—long, thin, parallel; Bean—broad, palmate.**
- Which plant has broad leaves? **Bean.**
- Which has long narrow leaves? **Corn.**
- Which plant is a monocot? **Corn.**
- Which plant is a dicot? **Bean.**

WHAT DID WE LEARN?

- What general shape of leaves do monocots and dicots have? **Monocots usually have long narrow leaves with parallel veins. Dicots usually have wider flat leaves with either pinnate or palmate veins. Evergreens usually have needles or scales for leaves.**
- How can we use leaves to help us identify plants? **Each plant has leaves with a unique shape and pattern. Some, such as the maple leaf, are very distinctive and easily recognizable. Others, grass for instance, can be more generic but can still be used to identify the species of plant.**
- How do nutrients and food get into and out of the leaves? **Xylem brings nutrients into the leaf, and then after the leaf has performed photosynthesis, the phloem transports the sugar from the leaves to the rest of the plant.**

TAKING IT FURTHER

- Describe how the arrangement of the veins is most efficient for each leaf shape. **Long, narrow leaves don't need veins that branch out, so parallel veins work well. Wider leaves need veins that reach out to the whole leaf, so palmate and pinnate veins are needed. For example, a maple leaf is nearly as wide as it is long, so a palmate arrangement of leaves is most efficient for transporting nutrients.**

LESSON 19

CHANGING COLORS

THE BEAUTY OF AUTUMN

SUPPLY LIST

If it is autumn, collect different colored leaves. If not, use several colors of construction paper

Scissors   Glue   Tag board/poster board   Newspaper   Heavy book

Supplies for Challenge: 2 or 3 different fresh leaves   Fingernail polish remover

Coffee filters   Quarter or other coin   Tape   Dish

BEGINNERS

- Why do trees lose their leaves in the fall? **To protect the trees from the winter cold.**
- How do trees know when it is time to lose their leaves? **There is less sunlight in the fall.**

- What causes the leaves to change colors in the fall? **The trees quit sending water up to the leaves, so the chlorophyll gets used up and other colors in the leaves become visible.**

WHAT DID WE LEARN?

- How do trees know when to change color? **The reduced amount of sunlight available each day signals the tree to begin preparing for winter.**

- Why do trees drop their leaves? **As protection from the cold weather.**

- Why don't evergreen trees drop their leaves in the winter? **Their leaves are not easily damaged by the cold so the tree can survive the winter without losing them.**

TAKING IT FURTHER

- Do trees and bushes with leaves that are purple in the summer still have chlorophyll? **Yes, but in smaller amounts compared to the red pigment.**

- What factors, other than daylight, might affect when a tree's leaves start changing color? **Temperature can affect it to some extent. Also, the amount of water available has some effect, but even when the fall is unusually warm the leaves still begin to change about the same time each year because of the shorter period of daylight.**

LESSON 20 TREE IDENTIFICATION

HOW DO I KNOW WHAT TREE IT IS?

FINAL PROJECT SUPPLY LIST

Tree field guide such as *Peterson's First Guide to Trees, Reader's Digest Field Guide of North America,* or *Trees of North America* by C. Frank Brockman

Zipper bags or other storage containers   Access to trees with leaves   Index cards

Colored pencils   Leaf press or heavy books and newspaper   Colored paper

Photo album with magnetic pages or 3-ring binder with plastic sheet protectors

Supplies for Challenge: Growth habit drawings from lesson 7

BEGINNERS

- Why can you use leaves to identify a tree? **Every tree's leaves have a unique shape.**

WHAT DID WE LEARN?

- What are some ways you can try to identify a plant? **By its leaves, flowers, fruit, bark, etc.**

- What are the biggest differences between deciduous and coniferous trees? **Deciduous trees have flowers, broad leaves and lose all their leaves each fall. Coniferous trees have cones and needles, and do not lose their needles each fall.**

TAKING IT FURTHER

- Why do we need to be able to identify trees and other plants? **To safely identify poisonous plants, to recognize ecosystems, for fun, to appreciate the diversity and wonder of God's creation and to make good landscaping choices.**

QUIZ 4

LEAVES

LESSONS 16–20

1. What is the purpose of the stomata in leaves? **To allow carbon dioxide in and oxygen out.**

2. For each leaf below, describe its vein arrangement (palmate or pinnate) and identify it if you can.
   A. Palmate—Maple   B. Pinnate—Oak   C. Pinnate—Ash   D. Pinnate—Holly

Short answer:

3. Which leaf above appears to be a compound leaf? **C.**

4. What kind of leaf arrangement does plant D have? **Alternate.**

5. How do leaves follow the sun? **The tips of the leaves detect the light and send out a chemical which makes the cells on the shady side get longer, thus turning the leaf toward the sun.**

6. What makes leaves green? **The chlorophyll in the chloroplasts.**

7. Identify the "ingredients" (beginning materials) and the "products" (ending materials) of photosynthesis. Ingredients: **Light, water, carbon dioxide, and chlorophyll;** Products: **Glucose/sugar and oxygen.**

CHALLENGE QUESTIONS

8. For each leaf above describe the leaf margin. **A. Lobed   B. Lobed   C. Toothed   D. Toothed**

9. Name two pigments that could be found in leaves. **Chlorophyll, carotene, xanthophyll, anthocyanin, etc.**

10. What is the chemical formula for photosynthesis? $6\,CO_2 + 6\,H_2O + light = C_6H_{12}O_6 + 6\,O_2$

11. What is the purpose of a bract? **To attract pollinators to the flowers.**

12. What is one purpose of a succulent leaf? **To store water, to perform photosynethesis.**

UNIT 5
FLOWERS & FRUITS

LESSON 21

FLOWERS

THE BEAUTY OF SIGHT AND SCENT

SUPPLY LIST

Copy of "Flower Pattern"   Green pipe cleaners   Flexible soda straws   Modeling clay
Colored construction paper   Scissors   Glue   Hole punch   Corn meal or yellow sand

BEGINNERS

- What are the four important parts of a plant? **Roots, stems, leaves, and flowers.**
- What are the four main parts of a flower? **Sepals, petals, stamens, and pistils.**

WHAT DID WE LEARN?

- What are the four parts of the flower and what is the purpose or job of each part? **The sepal protects the developing bud, the petals attract pollinators, the stamen produces pollen, and the pistil produces ovules that grow into seeds.**

TAKING IT FURTHER

- Why do you think God made so many different shapes and colors of flowers? **We enjoy the variety, and this shows us God's amazing creativity. Also, different animals are attracted by different colors and different scents. Hummingbirds are mainly attracted by red flowers, while other animals prefer different colors.**

LESSON 22

POLLINATION

THE BUZZING BEE'S JOB

SUPPLY LIST

Copy of the "Flip Book" worksheet   Crayons, markers, or colored pencils   Stapler
Bean and corn plants from lessons 8 and 9
Supplies for Challenge: Microscope and slide, if available   Pollen grains   Magnifying glass

BEGINNERS

- What is nectar? **A sweet liquid produced by the flower to attract insects.**

- What is pollination? **Moving pollen from one flower to another.**
- How does pollen get from one flower to another? **Bees and other insects move from flower to flower looking for nectar, and the pollen gets stuck to their bodies.**

WHAT DID WE LEARN?

- What animals can pollinate a flower? **Bees, wasps, moths, hummingbirds, bats, beetles, and even some small rodents can all be pollinators.**
- How can a flower be pollinated without an animal? **The wind or rain can move the pollen from the stamen to the pistil.**
- Does pollen have to come from another flower? **Not always, but it generally comes from another flower on another plant.**

TAKING IT FURTHER

- Why do you suppose God designed most plants to need cross-pollination? **The genetic information is stored in the pollen and ovules. If plants were always self-pollinated, much genetic information would be lost. The seeds formed from cross-pollination combine the hereditary traits of both parents, and the resulting offspring generally are more varied and often healthier than would be the case with self-pollination.**

LESSON 23

FLOWER DISSECTION

SEEING WHAT'S INSIDE

SUPPLY LIST

A fresh flower with easily-visible reproductive parts (A lily or an alstroemeria is a good example.)
Sharp knife or razor blade
Supplies for Challenge: Composite flower such as daisy, sunflower, or zinnia

BEGINNERS

- What is the job of the sepals? **To protect the developing flower.**
- What is the job of the petals? **To attract insects.**
- What is the job of the stamens? **To produce pollen.**
- What is the job of the pistil? **To receive pollen and make seeds.**

WHAT DID WE LEARN?

- How many ovules did you find? **Answers will vary.**
- What did they look like? **Answers will vary.**

TAKING IT FURTHER

- Why are the ovules in the flower green or white when most seeds are brown or black? **They are not fertilized and are not mature.**
- If you planted the ovules, would they grow into a plant? **No, they are not pollinated and are not mature or ready to grow into a plant.**

LESSON
24

FRUITS

IS IT RIPE YET?

SUPPLY LIST

Apple, strawberry, pineapple (all fresh and whole, if possible)　　Knife
Supplies for Challenge: Copy of "Fruit Classification" worksheet

BEGINNERS

- Name three fruits. **Answers will vary.**
- What is the job of the fruit? **To help the seeds get to a new location.**

WHAT DID WE LEARN?

- What is the main purpose of fruit? **To make sure the seeds are dispersed.**
- What are the three main groups of fruit? **Simple, aggregate, and multiple.**
- Describe how each type of fruit forms. **Simple fruit forms one fruit from one flower with one pistil. Aggregate fruit forms one fruit from one flower with several pistils. Multiple fruit forms one piece from several flowers with each fruit fusing together into a whole.**

TAKING IT FURTHER

- What is the fruit of a wheat plant? **The kernel of wheat that we make into flour.**
- Which category of fruit is most common? **Simple.**
- Why do biologists consider a green pepper to be a fruit? **They are the mature ovary of the plant. Any reproductive structure is a fruit. Other examples include beans, peas, tomatoes, and broccoli.**

CHALLENGE: FRUIT CLASSIFICATION WORKSHEET

1. _D_ Acorn
2. _E_ Pea
3. _C_ Pear
4. _A_ Avacado
5. _A_ Mango
6. _E_ Peanut
7. _E_ Lima bean
8. _F_ Wheat
9. _A_ Nectarine
10. _B_ Green pepper
11. _D_ Cashew
12. _C_ Crabapple
13. _B_ Grapefruit
14. _F_ Corn
15. _F_ Rice

WORLD OF PLANTS

ANNUALS, BIENNIALS, & PERENNIALS

HOW LONG DO THEY GROW?

SUPPLY LIST

Copy of "Plant Word Search"

BEGINNERS

- How long does it take for an annual plant to complete its lifecycle? **One year or one growing season.**
- What kinds of plants grow year after year? **Perennials, or trees and shrubs.**

PLANT WORD SEARCH

```
P H O T O S Y N T H E S I S S
H R S E E D S K Q E R T A L P
O G T E E S A A N N U A L V A
S T E R B T M C H R Y S E E S
T B M P H O R O S Y N I A C H
C H L O R O P H Y L L M V O P
Z O P O N P U P U W R F E T E
L H D R M A B I P R U L S Y R
V I P O L L I N A T I O N L E
O R A O C M E N T L A W Q E N
P I N T E A N A I P T E C D N
A B C S E T N T B A I R O O I
L E V B W E I E C C A S T N A
M A N V C P A R E S N I A L L
A F R U I T L D E M F R I U R
```

WHAT DID WE LEARN?

- What is an annual plant? **One that completes its lifecycle in one growing season.**
- What is a biennial plant? **One that completes its lifecycle in two growing seasons.**
- What is a perennial plant? **One that grows year after year, producing flowers and seeds each season.**

TAKING IT FURTHER

- Why don't we often see the flowers of biennial plants? **We usually harvest them the first season.**
- Why don't people grow new plants from the seeds produced by the annuals each year? **Often the conditions are not right for germination of the seeds produced the previous year. Also, many people clear their gardens of the dead flowers before the flowers have a chance to deposit their seeds. Finally, nurseries and greenhouses can begin growing plants inside much earlier than the plants would begin growing in the garden. This allows plants to be mature enough to be blooming by the beginning of spring. Plants that come up naturally in your garden would not bloom until much later in the summer, and people want to have blossoms in their gardens all spring and summer.**

QUIZ 5

FLOWERS & FRUITS

LESSONS 21–25

1. Match the labels to the parts of the flower below: a. **Pollen**, b. **Ovule**, c. **Ovary**, d. **Pistil**, e. **Petals**, f. **Stamen**, g. **Sepal**

Short answer:

2. Which part of the flower is considered the male part? **Stamen.**

3. Which part of the flower is considered the female part? **Pistil.**

4. How is a simple fruit different from an aggregate fruit? **Simple fruit forms one fruit from one flower with one pistil. Aggregate fruit forms one fruit from one flower with multiple pistils.**

5. Describe the process of pollination: **Pollen is removed from a stamen, usually by a pollinator like a bee or other insect. It is then deposited on the pistil of another flower. A pollen tube grows down into the ovary until it reaches the ovule. Fertilization takes place and the ovule becomes a seed.**

6. List two ways that pollen can be transferred from one flower to another. **Possible answers include: By an animal or other pollinator, by wind, rain, or by a person.**

7. How long does it take for a biennial to complete its lifecycle? **2 years or 2 growing seasons.**

CHALLENGE QUESTIONS

Mark each statement as either True or False.

8. _F_ Composite flowers have only one flower per stalk.

9. _T_ Ray flowers often look like petals.

10. _T_ Disk flowers produce hundreds of seeds.

11. _F_ Flowers do not need to attract pollinators.

12. _T_ Some nectar guides can normally only be seen by insects.

13. _T_ Some flowers smell bad to attract flies as pollinators.

14. _T_ Succulent fruits are simple fruits.

15. _T_ An olive is considered a fruit.

16. _F_ Peanuts are nuts.

17. _F_ Apples are berries from a biological definition.

18. _T_ Oranges are berries from a biological definition.

19. _F_ Ephemeral plants live for many years.

20. _T_ Ephemeral plants often live in the desert.

Unit 6
UNUSUAL PLANTS

LESSON 26

MEAT-EATING PLANTS

WILL IT EAT ME?

SUPPLY LIST

Small box   Stick or pole

Supplies for Challenge: Drawing materials

BEGINNERS

- What is the most famous meat-eating plant? **Venus flytrap.**
- How does a butterwort trap insects? **It has sticky leaves.**
- Why do some plants eat insects? **They do not get enough nutrients from the soil.**

WHAT DID WE LEARN?

- What is a carnivorous plant? **One that eats animals, usually insects.**
- Why do some plants need to be carnivorous? **Some plants grow in areas where there are not enough nutrients in the soil. They trap insects to get the necessary nutrients to survive.**
- How does a carnivorous plant eat an insect? **It traps the insect then secretes an acid that breaks down the animal's body so the nutrients can be absorbed.**

TAKING IT FURTHER

- Where are you likely to find carnivorous plants? **In wet, marshy areas.**
- How might a Venus flytrap tell the difference between an insect on its leaf and a raindrop? **The flytrap is designed with trigger bristles that have to be moved in order for the leaf to close. Two or more must be moved within a short period of time for the leaf to close. A raindrop might touch one but would probably not trigger two or more, but a moving insect would.**

LESSON 27

PARASITES & PASSENGERS

LIVING OFF OF EACH OTHER

SUPPLY LIST

Drinking straw   Coffee stirrer (a narrow straw)   Field guide to plants   Knife or scissors   Sink

Supplies for Challenge: Research materials—depends on your chosen topic

BEGINNERS

- What is a parasitic plant? **One that steals water and nutrients from another plant.**
- What is a passenger plant? **One that grows on the side of another plant without hurting it.**
- How does a passenger plant get water? **With special roots that absorb water from the air.**

WHAT DID WE LEARN?

- What is a parasitic plant? **One that gets its nourishment from another plant instead of making its own food.**
- What is a passenger plant? **One that lives on the outside of another plant without harming it.**
- How do passenger plants obtain water and minerals? **They absorb them from the air and from the surface of the host.**

TAKING IT FURTHER

- Where is the most likely place to find passenger plants? **On trees—often in the rain forest, but also in other areas.**
- Do passenger plants perform photosynthesis? **Yes, they still make their own food.**
- Do parasitic plants perform photosynthesis? **Some do but most do not. They get their food from the host plant.**

LESSON 28

TROPISMS

HOW PLANTS RESPOND

SUPPLY LIST

A houseplant with several leaves

Supplies for Challenge: Copy of "Tropisms" worksheet

BEGINNERS

- Will a plant grow upside down if the seed is planted upside down? **No, it will sense up and down and grow correctly.**
- What are some things that plants have the ability to sense? **Up and down, water and light.**
- What will a plant do if something blocks the light? **It will try to grow around it.**

WHAT DID WE LEARN?

- What is geotropism? **The ability of plant roots to always grow down and stems to grow up, a response to gravity.**
- What is hydrotropism? **The ability of plant roots to grow toward water, a response to water.**
- What is phototropism or heliotropism? **The ability of plant leaves to turn toward the sun or a light source, a response to light.**

TAKING IT FURTHER

- Why are tropisms sometimes called "survival techniques"? **They allow the plant to survive even if conditions change. They give the plant a better chance for survival even when water is scarce or something blocks the sun.**

- Will a seed germinate if it is planted 5 feet (1.5 m) from the water? **No, seeds need water to soften the seed coat and germinate. Tropisms only help the plant after germination.**

- Where are some places you would not want to plant water-seeking plants such as willows? **Near a swimming pool, septic tank, or water line.**

LESSON 29

SURVIVAL TECHNIQUES

SURVIVING IN HARSH CLIMATES

SUPPLY LIST

Cactus plant   Magnifying glass

Supplies for Challenge: Copy of "Designed for Survival" worksheet

BEGINNERS

- Name three ways that God has designed plants to be able to survive harsh conditions. **Cactus can store water in its stem; cactus has needles that do not lose water; mountain plants grow close to the ground to avoid wind; mountain plants grow in groups to keep each other warm.**

WHAT DID WE LEARN?

- How do some plants survive in hot, dry climates? **They quickly absorb the available water and store it in their expandable stems. They have needles instead of regular leaves so water does not evaporate quickly.**

- How do some plants survive in cold windy climates? **They have small leaves and short stems to withstand the wind. They grow low to the ground and in groups. They can reproduce very quickly.**

TAKING IT FURTHER

- Why do alpine plants need protection from the sun? **High in the mountains there is less atmosphere, so the sun's rays are more intense.**

CHALLENGE: DESIGNED FOR SURVIVAL WORKSHEET

- List six things that plants need to survive. **Light, warmth, water, carbon dioxide, oxygen, trace elements including nitrogen and phosphorus, and a place to grow.**

- List six things that can harm plants. **Wind, lack of water, hail, insects, diseases, over crowding, parasites, lack of light, and over watering.**

- List 12 ways that plants have been designed to survive. **Broad leaf trees lose their leaves in winter, seeds do not germinate until conditions are favorable for growth (seed dormancy), plants have seed distribution techniques, seeds store energy for the growing shoot, special roots including prop roots, aerial roots, pneumatophore roots, photosynthesis, leaf arrangement, leaf shape, flower shape, meat-eating plants' designs, special stems including tendrils, thorns, stolons and runners, parasitic designs, passenger plants can use other plants to help them survive without harming them, all the various tropisms, ability to** store water, needle-like leaves on cacti, design of alpine plants, bracts attract pollinators, scent, color, and pollen guides help attract pollinators .

- List four ways that people help plants to survive. **Water your grass, flowers, or other plants, add fertilizer to the soil, plant certain plants in a favorable location such as in the shade or sun depending on the plant, provide a trellis for climbing plants, pulling weeds to prevent competition, spray insecticide or fungicide, remove parasites, prune.**

REPRODUCTION WITHOUT SEEDS

THERE ARE OTHER WAYS

SUPPLY LIST

Potato   Jar   Potting soil   Water

Supplies for Challenge: Research materials on genetic modification

BEGINNERS

- Where do most new plants come from? **Seeds.**
- How do we get new strawberry plants? **Older plants send out special stems call runners that grow new plants.**
- How do we get new tulips? **The bulbs underground grow more bulbs.**

WHAT DID WE LEARN?

- What are some ways that plants can reproduce without growing from seeds? **Some plants reproduce by sending out runners, producing bulbs, or growing new plants from parts cut from the original plant.**

TAKING IT FURTHER

- Why can a potato grow from a piece of potato instead of from a seed? **All of the growth information is located in the eyes of the potato, so a new plant can grow from this area.**
- Will the new plant be just like the original plant? **Genetically, the new plant will be identical to the original plant. This is not the case with plants grown from seeds. Seeds contain genetic information from both the plant producing the pollen and the plant producing the ovule, but plants grown vegetatively only get genes from the original plant.**

FERNS

SEEDLESS PLANTS

SUPPLY LIST

Paper   Paint and paint brushes   Glue   Corn meal or yellow sand
Fresh fern frond, if available

BEGINNERS

- How do plants without flowers grow new plants? **They produce spores.**
- What is one plant that produces spores? **Ferns.**
- Where do ferns grow? **In areas with lots of rain.**

WHAT DID WE LEARN?

- How are ferns like other plants? **They have chlorophyll, stems, leaves, and roots.**
- What are fern leaves called? **Fronds.**
- How are ferns different from other plants? **They do not have flowers or seeds.**
- How do they reproduce? **They make spores on the back of their fronds that produce an egg and sperm that combine and grow into a tiny new plant.**

TAKING IT FURTHER

- Why can't ferns reproduce with seeds? **They do not produce flowers, so they cannot make seeds.**

LESSON 32

MOSSES

DO YOU REALLY FIND MOSS ON THE NORTH SIDE OF TREES?

SUPPLY LIST

Paper and glue   Colored pencils or crayons   Dried moss from a craft shop   Magnifying glass
Supplies for Challenge: Peat mos   Dirt or soil from your yard   Paper cups

BEGINNERS

- How big are moss plants? **They are very small.**
- What plant parts do mosses have? **Leaves and stems and something like roots.**
- How do moss plants reproduce? **With spores.**
- Where do moss plants grow? **Anywhere that is wet.**

WHAT DID WE LEARN?

- How do mosses differ from seed-bearing plants? **They have no flowers, seeds, or true roots.**
- How do mosses differ from ferns? **They are smaller, have no true roots, and produce their spores on stalks instead of on their leaves.**
- How do mosses produce food? **They have chlorophyll and perform photosynthesis just like other plants do.**

TAKING IT FURTHER

- Are you likely to find moss in a desert? Why/why not? **No. There is not enough moisture in the desert for moss to grow well.**

LESSON 33

ALGAE

ARE ALL GREEN THINGS PLANTS?

SUPPLY LIST

Paper   Colored pencils   Glue   Construction paper   Scissors
Supplies for Challenge: Sample of pond water   Microscope and slide

BEGINNERS

- How are algae similar to plants? **They have chlorophyll and perform photosynthesis, but they have no leaves, stems, or roots.**
- Why are algae important? **They produce food for the sea creatures and most of the oxygen on the planet.**

WHAT DID WE LEARN?

- Why are algae such important organisms? **They produce large amounts of oxygen and they are the major source of food in many aquatic food chains.**
- What gives algae its green color? **Chlorophyll.**

TAKING IT FURTHER

- Why are some algae yellow, brown, blue, or red? **All algae have chlorophyll, but like many other plants, some have other pigments as well, which often cover up the green of the chlorophyll.**

LESSON 34

FUNGI

ARE THESE REALLY PLANTS?

SUPPLY LIST

6 slices of bread (homemade works best)   3 plastic sandwich bags or plastic zipper bags
Copy of "Mold Data Sheet"
Supplies for Challenge: Fresh mushroom   Index card   Aerosol hairspray

BEGINNERS

- Are mushrooms plants? **No, they are fungi.**
- Name three kinds of fungi. **Mushrooms, mold, and yeast.**
- What is one way that fungi can be bad? **Some are poisonous, some cause disease, and some spoil food.**
- What is one way that fungi can be good? **Some are good to eat, yeast makes bread fluffy, some give cheese its special flavor, some get rid of dead plants and animals.**

What did we learn?

- Why are fungi not considered plants and given their own kingdom? **Fungi do not have chlorophyll and do not have roots, stems, and leaves as plants do.**

- What are some good uses for fungi? **Fungi are used for food, to make bread rise, to make medicines, to give cheese its flavor, and to help in the recycling of dead plants and animals.**

Taking it further

- What other conditions might affect mold growth other than those tested here? **Light/dark or the presence of chemicals like the preseratives found in foods.**

- How can you keep your bread from becoming moldy? **Keep it in a cool dry place.**

QUIZ 6

UNUSUAL PLANTS

LESSONS 26–34

Match the term with its definition.

1. _C_ Plants that eat insects
2. _B_ Plants that "steal" nutrients from other plants
3. _D_ Plants that grow on other plants without harming them
4. _A_ Response of plants to gravity, roots go down, stems go up
5. _E_ Tendency for roots to grow toward water
6. _G_ Ability of leaves to turn toward sunlight
7. _F_ Plant designed to store available water in dry conditions
8. _G_ Plant reproduction using a part of the plant (not seeds)
9. _H_ Runners from a strawberry plant
10. _I_ Special stems that grow underground for reproduction

Short answer:

11. What plant organ is missing in ferns? **Flowers.**
12. How do both mosses and ferns reproduce? **Spores.**
13. What two plant organs are missing in mosses? **Flowers and true roots.**
14. What substance do algae have in common with plants? **Chlorophyll.**
15. What is the name of the group that contains yeast and mushrooms? **Fungi.**

CHALLENGE QUESTIONS

Accept reasonable answers for all challenge questions.

16. Give an example of positive tropism. **Hydrotropism, phototropism, and geotropism for roots.**

17. Give an example of negative tropism. **Geotropism for stems, thermotropism for curling leaves, and thigmotropism for roots.**

18. Explain how a cobra lily traps insects. **It attracts insects to its pitcher with nectar, then as the insect tries to find the exit it hits the top of the pitcher and falls inside.**

19. Explain how succulents are designed to survive dry periods. **They can store large amounts of water in their stems and/or leaves.**

20. Why is grafting a form of cloning? **The resulting plant has identical DNA to the parent plant.**

21. Where would you likely find the stems of a fern plant? **Underground.**

22. Give one reason why peat moss is important. **It holds water and increases the moisture of the soil, it can be used for fuel, and mosses create new soil and return nutrients to the soil .**

23. Give one commercial use of algae. **Scrubbing agent, makes many items creamy, used as a food, and thickens ice cream and other products.**

FINAL EXAM

WORLD OF PLANTS

LESSONS 1–34

Define each of the following terms.

1. Geotropism: **Response of plant to gravity; causes roots to grow down and stems to grow up.**

2. Hydrotropism: **Response of plants to water; causes roots to grow toward a source of water.**

3. Phototropism: **Response of plants to light; leaves turn toward the sun.**

4. Photosynthesis: **Process by which sunlight, chlorophyll, carbon dioxide, and water are turned into sugar and oxygen.**

5. Pollination: **Process by which pollen is transferred from one flower to another to cause the fertilization of the ovule, thereby creating seeds.**

6. Chlorophyll: **The green substance in plant cells that is used to perform photosynthesis.**

7. Ovule: **The egg or unfertilized seed found in the ovary of the flower.**

8. Pistil: **The female part of the flower that produces ovules.**

9. Stamen: **The male part of the flower that produces pollen.**

10. Xylem and phloem: **The tubes that carry nutrients, food, and water throughout the plant.**

Choose the best answer for each question.

11. _C_ Which of the following is not an organ of flowering plants?

12. _D_ Which kind or kinds of creatures get nourishment from grasses?

13. _A_ Which is not a common use for the wood of a tree?

14. _B_ Which tree is a deciduous tree?

15. _C_ Which organ is primarily used to absorb minerals from the ground?

Fill in the blank with the correct term.

16. Root growth primarily occurs at the **_root tip or root cap_**.

17. The two types of root systems are **_fibrous_** and **_taproot_**.

18. The shape of most monocot plants' leaves is **_long and thin like grass_**.

19. Ferns reproduce by **_spores_** on their leaves.

20. Algae are similar to plants because they contain **_chlorophyll_**.

Mark each statement as either True or False.

21. _F_ Plants with red leaves have no chlorophyll.

22. _T_ Trees can be identified by their leaves.

23. _F_ Coniferous trees do not have leaves.

24. _F_ The scent of a flower has no purpose.

25. _T_ Ferns are not flowering plants.

26. _T_ Algae is an important organism.

27. _T_ Sepals might be confused with leaves.

28. _T_ Pollination must take place for seeds to form.

29. _T_ Mosses reproduce by spores and not seeds.

30. _T_ Photosynthesis cannot take place without chlorophyll.

CHALLENGE QUESTIONS

Match the term with its definition.

30. _E_ Law of biogenesis

31. _C_ Meiosis

32. _A_ Spontaneous generation

33. _D_ Scarification

34. _F_ Stratification

35. _B_ Seed dormancy

36. _K_ Primary growth

37. _J_ Secondary growth

38. _G_ Osmosis

39. _H_ Toothed leaf margin

40. _I_ Lobed leaf margin

Mark each statement as either True or False.

41. _F_ Ephemeral plants grow slowly.

42 _T_ Composite flowers are really hundreds of flowers grouped together.

43. _F_ Legumes have hard outer shells.

44. _T_ Pomes have papery inner cores.

45. _T_ Chemotropism aids in pollination.

46. _T_ Filament algae is very common.

47. _F_ Most fruit trees are grown from seeds.

48. _F_ Tendrils have negative tropism.

49. _T_ Rootstock is important for grafting.

50. _F_ There are very few commercial uses for algae.

LESSON 35

CONCLUSION

APPRECIATING THE WORLD OF PLANTS

SUPPLY LIST

Tag board   Dried leaves, flowers, grass   Glue   Seeds, seed pods, other parts of plants

THE WORLD OF ANIMALS

MAMMALS

LESSON 1

THE WORLD OF ANIMALS

IS IT A MOUSE OR A MOOSE?

SUPPLY LIST

Note: Throughout this book you may wish to have additional resources with color pictures and information about each group of animals being studied. Animal encyclopedias or other resources, such as the Answers in Genesis *Zoo Guide* and *Aquarium Guide*, can be valuable in enhancing the lessons.

BEGINNERS

- How many different types of animals are there? **At least 1 million.**
- What are the two big groups of animals? **Vertebrates and invertebrates.**
- Who made all the different animals? **God did.**

WHAT DID WE LEARN?

- What are the two major divisions of animals? **Vertebrates and invertebrates.**
- What are two similarities among all animals? **They move and they must eat plants or other animals.**

TAKING IT FURTHER

- When did God create the different animal kinds? **On Day Five of creation God created fish and birds; on Day Six He created land animals. See Genesis 1.**
- How is man different from animals? **Humans have a conscience so they can tell right from wrong; animals act on instinct. People have a spirit so they can have a relationship with God; animals do not. People were made in God's image; animals were not. Despite our physical similarities, people are spiritually very different from animals. God gave man dominion over the animals. See Genesis 1:28.**

LESSON 2

VERTEBRATES

DOES IT HAVE A BACKBONE?

SUPPLY LIST

3-ring binder   12 or more dividers with tabs
Supplies for Challenge: Drawing materials

BEGINNERS

- What are two things that all vertebrates have? **A backbone, a brain, a spinal cord, and bones.**
- What are the five different kinds of vertebrates? **Mammals, birds, fish, reptiles, and amphibians.**

WHAT DID WE LEARN?

- What are the two major divisions of the animal kingdom? **Vertebrates and invertebrates.**
- What characteristics define an animal as a vertebrate? **Vertebrates have a spinal cord ending in a brain protected by a backbone. They also have internal skeletons.**
- What are the five groups of vertebrates? **Mammals, birds, amphibians, reptiles, and fish.**

TAKING IT FURTHER

- Think about pictures you have seen of dinosaur skeletons. Do you think dinosaurs were vertebrates or invertebrates? Why do you think that? **Dinosaurs were vertebrates. This is shown by the fact that dinosaurs have internal skeletons and these skeletons contain vertebrae along the backs of the animals.**

LESSON 3 MAMMALS

THE FUZZY CREATURES

SUPPLY LIST

Copy of "Mammals Have Fur" worksheet   Samples of hair from as many mammals as possible
Book showing pictures of different mammals

Suggestions for animal books: *Magnificent Mammals* by Buddy and Kay Davis, and *Kingfisher Illustrated Animal Encyclopedia.*

BEGINNERS

- What are five things that all mammals have in common? **They have hair, give birth to live young, nurse their young, are warm-blooded, and breathe air with lungs.**
- Name three mammals that have not been mentioned in this lesson. **Answers will vary.**

WHAT DID WE LEARN?

- What five characteristics are common to all mammals? **They are warm-blooded, breathe with lungs, give birth to live young, nurse their young, and have hair or fur.**
- Why do mammals have hair? **To keep them warm, to aid in the sense of touch, and for some it provides camouflage.**
- Why is a platypus considered a mammal even though it lays eggs? **It nurses its young.**

TAKING IT FURTHER

- Name some ways that mammals regulate their body temperature. **Mammals cool down by sweating or panting. They heat up by eating, exercising, or covering their bodies to keep warm.**
- What are some animals that have hair that helps them hide from their enemies? **Tigers and zebras have stripes that make them hard to see. Lions are the color of their surroundings.**

CHALLENGE: MAMMAL FEET

Deer: **Unguligrade**   Rabbit: **Plantigrade**   Giraffe: **Unguligrade**

Wolf: **Digitigrade**   Skunk: **Plantigrade**   Elephant: **Unguligrade**

Opossum: **Plantigrade**   Chimpanzee: **Plantigrade**   Fox: **Digitigrade**

LESSON 4
MAMMALS LARGE & SMALL
ARMADILLO TO ZEBRA

SUPPLY LIST

Drawing paper   Markers, colored pencils or paint

BEGINNERS

- Name three large mammals. **Elephants, giraffes, bears, and horses.**
- Name three small mammals. **Pika, mice, voles, hamsters, and gerbils.**
- Name one mammal that can fly. **Bat.**
- Name one mammal that can lay eggs. **Spiny anteater or platypus.**

WHAT DID WE LEARN?

- What is the largest land mammal? **Elephant.**
- What is the tallest land mammal? **Giraffe.**
- What do bears eat? **Nearly anything, but they prefer plants, roots, and berries.**

TAKING IT FURTHER

- What do you think is the most fascinating mammal? Why do you think that? **Answers will vary.**

LESSON 5
MONKEYS & APES
PRIMATES

SUPPLY LIST

Copy of "Mammals Word Search"

BEGINNERS

- What group of mammals are monkeys a part of? **Primates.**
- What is the difference between monkeys and apes? **Apes do not have tails and monkeys do.**
- Where do monkeys spend most of their time? **In the trees.**
- What kinds of food do monkeys eat? **Fruits, flowers, and insects.**

Mammals Word Search

```
D G E U T A F R O P K L H Y U
B E N D R M L J I O S C X F A
A Z E B R A Z C V B C A B S R
M N I D S M F V G F T T J A E
S R E I H M U X A A I M U P U
C O L S W A R M B L O O D E D
C A M E L R H O P T W U P E A
K E Y M O Y U S P Z E S R R W
F R L U G G D R W R G E K H U
M L U L E L I V E B I R T H S
O U E N A A T G L A R M D O B
C N H M O N K E Y V A I A N P
F G Y B U D L E W C F A N T L
H S A L E R U P Q Z F L U H E
R A J C J K W H A L E E S O P
```

What did we learn?

- What are two common characteristics of all primates? **They have five fingers and five toes, and eyes on the fronts of their heads giving them binocular vision.**

- What are the three groups of primates? **Monkeys, apes, and prosimians.**

- What is one difference between apes and monkeys? **Apes do not have tails, monkeys do. Also, an ape's arms are longer than its legs, but this is not true for monkeys.**

- Where do New World Monkeys live? **In the western hemisphere.**

- Where do Old World Monkeys live? **In the eastern hemisphere.**

- What is a prehensile tail? **A tail that can grasp onto things.**

Taking it further

- If a monkey lives in South America is it likely to have a prehensile tail? **Yes, because New World Monkeys have prehensile tails and Old World Monkeys do not.**

- Are you more likely to find a monkey or an ape in a tree in the rain forest? **You are more likely to find a monkey in a tree. Many apes do not spend a lot of time in trees, whereas most monkeys live the majority of their lives in trees.**

- Why do most prosimians have very large eyes? **The majority of prosimians are nocturnal, that is, they sleep during the day and are awake at night. Large eyes allow these animals to see better at night.**

LESSON

6 Aquatic Mammals

They live in the water?

Supply list

Toothbrush   Stop watch   Chopped nuts, fruits, or vegetables   2 cups   Water

BEGINNERS

- What is different about how dolphins and whales breathe compared to how fish breathe? **Dolphins and whales breathe air while fish breathe water.**
- What is different about how dolphins and whales feed their babies compared to how fish feed their babies? **Dolphins and whales feed milk to their young and fish do not.**
- What special feature did God give to dolphins and whales to help them breathe? **Blowhole.**

WHAT DID WE LEARN?

- Why are dolphins and whales considered mammals and not fish? **They are warm-blooded, give birth to live young, nurse their babies and breathe air with lungs.**
- What is the main difference between the tails of fish and the tails of aquatic mammals? **Fish tails move from side to side and mammal tails, or flukes, move up and down.**
- What is another name for a manatee? **Sea cow.**
- Why are manatees sometimes called sea cows? **They move slowly and graze on sea grass and other sea plants just like a cow grazing in a field.**

TAKING IT FURTHER

- How has God specially designed aquatic mammals for breathing air? **First, He gave them blowholes or nostrils on the tops of their heads so it is easy to breathe while still being in the water. Second, He designed them to be able to stay submerged for several minutes or even an hour at a time so they do not have to stay near the surface. God also gave them flukes to help them resurface quickly.**
- What do you think might be one of the first things a mother whale or dolphin must teach a newborn baby? **One of the first things the mother will do is push the baby toward the surface of the water so it can get its first breath.**

LESSON

7 MARSUPIALS

POUCHED ANIMALS

SUPPLY LIST

Plastic zipper bag   Glue   Tag board or cardboard   Scissors   Fake fur or felt
Construction paper
Supplies for Challenge: Copy of "Koala Fun Facts" worksheet   Book or internet sites on koalas

BEGINNERS

- What feature is special about a marsupial? **It has a pouch.**
- What is a new born marsupial called? **A joey.**
- Name three marsupials. **Some of the more common marsupials include the kangaroo, koala, opossum, numbat, and Tasmanian devil.**
- What time of the day are kangaroos usually awake? **At night.**

What did we learn?

- What is a marsupial? **An animal that gives birth to very tiny underdeveloped young. The young then spend the next several months developing in the mother's pouch.**

- Name at least three marsupials? **Some of the more common marsupials include kangaroos, koalas, opossums, numbats, and Tasmanian devils.**

- How has God designed the kangaroo for jumping? **A kangaroo has large powerful hind legs, large hind feet and long stretchy tendons that help conserve energy when hopping.**

Taking it further

- About half of a kangaroo's body weight is from muscle. This is nearly twice as much as in most animals its size. How might this fact contribute to its ability to hop? **Large muscles are needed to provide the strength to hop long distances. So a kangaroo has very large leg muscles.**

- How do you think a joey kangaroo keeps from falling out of its mother's pouch when she hops? **The nipple swells when the joey first attaches so it cannot slip off. Also, the pouch has muscles that can contract like a drawstring to keep the pouch closed.**

Koala Fun Facts

- We often hear a koala referred to as a koala bear, but it is not a bear. List three ways that a koala is different from a bear. **Koalas have pouches and give birth to very immature/undeveloped young; koalas only live in Australia; koalas live in trees and bears do not; koalas do not hibernate or sleep through the winter.**

- What is unusual about the koala's pouch? **It opens toward the back.**

- What does a baby koala eat? **Its mother's milk.**

- What does an adult koala eat? **Eucalyptus leaves.**

- What special design features make koalas able to eat this kind of food? **They have special grinding teeth, they have bacteria in their stomachs that help them digest the leaves.**

- How long does a baby koala spend in its mother's pouch? **6 months.**

- How does the mother koala carry her youngster after it leaves the pouch? **On her back.**

- What is special about the skin on the koala's feet that helps it to climb trees? **It is rough—friction skin—that grips even smooth trees.**

- What is special about the koala's hands that help it survive? **It has thumbs that grasp trees and leaves.**

- How much does a koala sleep? **Up to 20 hours a day.**

- About how much does an adult koala weigh? **19–33 pounds.**

- What is the average life span of a koala? **10–15 years.**

QUIZ 1

MAMMALS

LESSONS 1–7

Short answer:

1. What are the two main groups of animals? **Vertebrates and invertebrates.**
2. What are the five major groups of vertebrates? **Mammals, birds, amphibians, reptiles, fish.**

3. What are five common characteristics of mammals? **Warm-blooded, breathe air with lungs, fur/hair, live birth, nurse young.**

4. What makes a marsupial different from other mammals? **Has a pouch**.

5. What makes a vertebrate unique? **Has a spinal cord ending in a brain, backbone.**

Mark each statement as either True or False.

6. _F_ Animals can produce their own food.

7. _F_ Dolphins are large fish.

8. _T_ Marsupials give birth to tiny live babies

9. _F_ Baleen whales have large teeth.

10. _F_ The elephant is the largest animal in the world. **Note: Elephants are the largest land animal, but blue whales are the largest animal on earth.**

11. _T_ Monkeys have tails but apes do not.

12. _T_ Marsupials live primarily in Australia and Tasmania.

13. _T_ Some marsupials are meat-eating animals.

14. _T_ A lemur is a primate.

15. _F_ Primates have eyes on the sides of their heads.

CHALLENGE QUESTIONS

Short answer:

16. Draw a foot of a mammal to represent each of the following stances:

    Unguligrade: **Any animals with a hoof—horse, deer, or elephant.**

    Digitigrade: **Any animal that walks on its toes—dog, cat, wolf, or fox.**

    Plantigrade: **Any animal that walks on flat feet—rabbit, skunk, opossum, monkey, or bear.**

17. Match the parts of a ruminant's digestive system with its definition.

    _A_ Rumen _E_ Abomasum _C_ Cud _B_ Reticulum _D_ Omasum

18. List three special design features that God gave whales. **Blowhole separate from mouth, ability to regulate temperature with fins, ability to regulate blood pressure/body pressure when diving, ability to shut down unnecessary functions while feeding, echolocation, ability to expand throat when eating.**

19. List three special design features that God gave koalas. **Ability to eat and digest leaves, special teeth, bacteria in stomach, friction skin on feet for climbing, thumbs for grasping, pouch for babies.**

20. Explain why an ape doing sign language does not necessarily support the evolution of man from apes. **Many animals have some level of intelligence, but none are close to humans. More importantly, humans have a spirit that relates to God. Sign language does not necessarily demonstrate humanity.**

Unit 2
Birds & Fish

Lesson 8

Birds

Fine feathered friends

Supply list

Copy of "Bird Beaks & Bird Feet" worksheet   Bird guides or encyclopedias
Supplies for Challenge: Animal or bird encyclopedias

Beginners

*   What feature makes birds different from all other animals? **They have feathers.**
*   How do birds breathe? **The breathe air with lungs.**
*   How do birds give birth? **They lay eggs.**
*   How did God make birds' beak and feet to help them survive? **Accept reasonable answers.**

What did we learn?

*   How do birds differ from mammals? **Birds have feathers and wings, lay eggs, and usually can fly.**
*   How are birds the same as mammals? **They are both warm-blooded and breathe with lungs.**

Taking it further

*   How can you identify one bird from another? **By their size, shape, color of feathers, beak and feet shape, calls, and songs.**
*   What birds can you identify near your home? **Use a field guide to help you.**
*   Why might you see different birds near your home in the summer than in the winter? **Many birds migrate to live in a warmer area in the winter and a cooler area in the summer, so different birds may be in your area at different times of the year.**

Challenge: Birds vs. Reptiles

*   List some characteristics that may vary among a species due to natural selection. Look through an animal encyclopedia to see examples of these characteristic. Notice that not one of these various characteristics has resulted in a new species. **Color, size and shape of beaks, size and shape of legs, size of body, coloring of feathers.**

WORLD OF ANIMALS

LESSON 9

FLIGHT

HOW DO THOSE BIRDS DO THAT?

SUPPLY LIST

Copy of "God Designed Birds to Fly" worksheet   1 or more bird feathers
Magnifying glass

BEGINNERS

- Name three things that help a bird to fly. **Strong breast muscles, stiff backbone, air spaces in bones, shape of wing, feathers, and tail.**

- Why is it important that a bird's feathers point toward the back of the bird? **This helps air to flow smoothly over the feathers.**

- How does a bird use its tail while it is flying? **It moves its tail back and forth to steer.**

GOD DESIGNED BIRDS TO FLY WORKSHEET

- **Pictures should be similar to those in the student manual, pages 43–44.**

WHAT DID WE LEARN?

- What are some ways birds are designed for flight? **They have strong breast muscles, rigid backbones, hollow bones, efficient respiratory systems, feathers and wings.**

- What are the three kinds of bird feathers? **Down, contour, and flight feathers.**

- How does a bird repair a feather that is pulled open? **By preening—running the feather through its beak to re-hook the barbs.**

- How does a bird's tail work like a rudder? **It is moved from side to side to help steer.**

TAKING IT FURTHER

- Why can't man fly by strapping wings to his arms? **Man is not designed for flight. He does not have the strong breast muscles and stiff backbone needed. Humans are also too heavy to lift themselves with their arms.**

- How do you think birds use their feathers to stay warm? **Birds can fluff up their feathers and trap air under and between them. The heat from their bodies warms the trapped air, creating a barrier between their bodies and the cold air around them.**

- How is an airplane wing like a bird's wing? **They both have the same airfoil shape that allows the air flowing over the wing to create lift. Also, airplane wings are designed with the ability to change shape for different conditions, just like birds' wings.**

LESSON 10

THE BIRD'S DIGESTIVE SYSTEM

THEY SURE EAT A LOT

SUPPLY LIST

Copy of "God Designed the Bird's Digestive System" worksheet   Owl pellet (optional)

BEGINNERS

- Why do birds spend most of their time eating? **They need lots of energy for flying.**
- Do birds chew up their food? **No, they don't have any teeth.**
- How does a bird's food get ground up? **Muscles in the gizzard grind the food.**

GOD DESIGNED THE BIRD'S DIGESTIVE SYSTEM WORKSHEET

- **See illustration in student manual, page 47.**

WHAT DID WE LEARN?

- How does a bird "chew" its food without teeth? **God designed birds with an organ called a gizzard, which grinds the food up internally. In addition, some birds swallow small stones or pebbles that help to grind up the food as well.**
- What purposes does the crop serve? **It holds the food so a bird can eat quickly. It then releases the food to be digested in a constant stream to provide a more constant source of energy.**

TAKING IT FURTHER

- How is a bird's digestive system different from a human digestive system? **A bird has a crop and a gizzard; humans do not. A bird does not have a large intestine. A bird's digestive system digests food much more quickly.**
- How does a bird's digestive system help it to be a better flyer? **Because the food is digested quickly and efficiently, more energy is available for flying. Because the food is digested at a constant rate, a steady source of energy is provided for extended flying.**

LESSON 11

FISH

DO FISH GO TO SCHOOL?

SUPPLY LIST

Goldfish snack crackers   Paper   Glue   Colored pencils

BEGINNERS

- Where do fish live? **In the water.**
- What do fish have covering their bodies? **Scales.**

- Are fish warm-blooded or cold-blooded? **Cold-blooded.**
- How do fish breathe? **They have gills that take oxygen out of the water.**
- How do most fish reproduce? **They usually lay eggs.**

WHAT DID WE LEARN?

- What makes fish different from other animals? **They live in the water, are cold-blooded, and have gills and scales.**
- How do fish breathe? **They get oxygen from the water using gills.**
- Why do some sharks have to stay in motion? **They must have a constant flow of water over their gills to breathe, and the only way they can do that is to swim with their mouths open.**
- What is the difference between warm-blooded and cold-blooded animals? **Warm-blooded animals regulate their body temperature—it stays the same regardless of the surrounding temperature. Cold-blooded animals cannot regulate their body temperature—it goes up and down with the surrounding temperature.**

TAKING IT FURTHER

- Other than how they breathe, how are dolphins different from fish? **Dolphins are warm-blooded, give birth to live young, nurse their young, have hair, and do not have scales.**
- How are dolphins like fish? **They live in the water, swim, have fins and a tail, and eat fish.**

CHALLENGE: DESIGNED FOR WATER

- Shape: **Fish that are flattened side to side can swim faster—slip through the water easily. Fish that are flattened top to bottom—can hide easily on the sea floor. Fish that are snake-like—can slip into crevices.**
- Scales: **Are an outgrowth of skin, arranged like shingles to provide protection, produce slime to fight fungus and allow for smoother movement through the water.**
- Color: **Fish are colored to blend into their environment, some can change their colors.**
- Gills: **efficiently remove oxygen from the water.**
- Eyes: **No eyelids, rigid lens that move forward and backward to focus, limited focusing is needed underwater.**
- Swim bladders: **Provide buoyancy.**

LESSON 12 FINS & OTHER FISH ANATOMY

DESIGNED FOR EFFICIENCY

SUPPLY LIST

Copy of "Fish Fins" worksheet   Construction paper   Scissors   Glue

BEGINNERS

- What is special about a fish body that helps it be a good swimmer? **Its shape, mucous, and fins.**
- How do the front fins help the fish? **They help it go up and down and to slow down.**
- How do the top and back fins help the fish? **They keep it from tipping sideways.**
- How does the tail help the fish? **It pushes it forward through the water.**

Fish Fins worksheet

- **See illustration in student manual, page 53.**

What did we learn?

- What is the purpose of a swim bladder? **It gives the fish buoyancy. When it fills with air, it makes the fish lighter than the water, allowing it to rise. When the air is released, the fish becomes heavier than the water and it sinks. This buoyancy keeps the fish floating without having to keep moving its fins.**

- How did God design the fish to be such a good swimmer? **The shape of its body, its fins, and the mucus on its body all help it to be an efficient swimmer.**

Taking it further

- How does mucus make a fish a more efficient swimmer? **Since mucus is slippery, it reduces friction so the fish does not have to work as hard to move through the water. To see how this works, put your hand under some running water and watch how the water flows. Then, rub a little cooking oil on your hand and repeat the test. The water flows more quickly over your oily hand because there is less friction.**

- How has man used the idea of a swim bladder in his inventions? **Submarines use air to help keep them afloat at the desired depth. Also, life rafts fill with air to help them float to the top of the water.**

- What other function can fins have besides helping with swimming? **Fins can provide protection from predators. Fins can make it difficult for a predator to swallow a fish. In addition, some fins are shaped and colored to help provide camouflage.**

- What similar design did God give to both fish and birds to help them get where they are going? **They both have rudder-like tails that help them steer, and bodies specially shaped for moving through their environments.**

LESSON 13 Cartilaginous Fish

No bones about it!

Supply list

Modeling clay
Supplies for Challenge: Pictures of cartilaginous fish

Beginners

- How is a shark's skeleton different from other fish skeletons? **It is made of cartilage instead of bone.**

- What happens when a shark's teeth wear out? **They are replaced by a new row of teeth.**

- How does a ray use its fins to swim? **It flaps them like wings.**

What did we learn?

- How do cartilaginous fish differ from bony fish? **Their skeletons are made from cartilage instead of bone. Also, many of these fish do not have the typical torpedo-shaped body.**

- Why is a lamprey called a parasite? **It does not eat prey. Instead, it attaches its mouth to a living animal, usually a fish, and sucks its blood for nutrients.**

- Why can sharks and stingrays be dangerous to humans? **Sharks can attack with their sharp teeth and stingrays can sting with their tails.**

TAKING IT FURTHER

- Why are shark babies born independent? **Like many other animals, sharks do not care for their young, so the babies must be able to care for themselves at birth. Many adult sharks will eat young sharks, so babies must avoid adults until they are large enough to defend themselves.**

- What do you think is the shark's biggest natural enemy? **Other sharks.**

BIRDS & FISH

LESSONS 8–13

Short answer:

1. Look at each picture of birds' feet below. Next to each picture write the word you think is most appropriate: **A. Perching B. Bird of prey C. Runner D. Water**

2. Look at each picture of birds' beaks below. Next to each picture write what you think that bird is likely to eat: **A. Water plants B. Nectar C. Water seeds D. Other animals**

3. List three ways that birds were specially designed for flight. **Strong breast muscles, stiff backbone, hollow bones, efficient digestive and respiratory systems, and feathers.**

4. List two special design features of a bird's digestive system. **It is very fast and efficient, crop releases food at a constant rate, and gizzard grinds food.**

5. Name three kinds of fins found on most fish. **Pectoral, pelvic, dorsal, anal, caudal.**

6. Name two kinds of cartilaginous fish. **Sharks, rays, hagfish, and lampreys.**

CHALLENGE QUESTIONS

Mark each statement as either True or False.

7. _T_ Animals can adapt to changes in their surroundings.

8. _F_ Birds evolved from reptiles.

9. _F_ Birds and reptiles are both cold-blooded animals.

10. _T_ Scales are very different from feathers.   .

11. _T_ There can be great variety among species.

12. _F_ Flightless birds have useless wings.

13. _T_ Kiwi birds lay eggs that are very large compared to their body size.

14. _T_ Penguins only live in the southern hemisphere.

15. _T_ Birds have a very efficient respiratory system.

16. _F_ Birds have a bellows type of respiratory system.

17. _T_ Some fish can change color.

18. _T_ Some fish can sense things that other animals cannot.

19. _F_ Fish have very small olfactory lobes compared to their brain size.

20. _T_ There are over 600 species of cartilaginous fish.

AMPHIBIANS & REPTILES

LESSON 14

AMPHIBIANS

AIR OR WATER?

SUPPLY LIST (none)

BEGINNERS

- Name three kinds of animals that are amphibians. **Frogs, toads, salamanders, and newts.**

- How does an amphibian breathe as a baby? **It breathes water with gills.**

- How does an amphibian breathe as an adult? **It breathes air with lungs.**

WHAT DID WE LEARN?

- What are the characteristics that make amphibians unique? **They spend part of their lives in water breathing with gills, and part of their lives on land breathing with lungs. They are also cold-blooded, usually have smooth moist skin and lay eggs.**

- How can you tell a frog from a toad? **In general, frogs have smooth moist skin, while toads have dry bumpy skin.**

- How can you tell a salamander from a lizard? **Salamanders have smooth skin and lizards have dry scales on their skin. Also, salamanders go through a larval stage but lizards do not.**

TAKING IT FURTHER

- What advantages do cold-blooded animals have over warm-blooded animals? **They don't have to eat as often and can usually survive a broader range of temperatures.**

- What advantages do warm-blooded animals have over cold-blooded animals? **Cold-blooded animals' activities are more restricted by temperature extremes. A warm-blooded animal can still be quite active in very cold or very warm weather.**

- Why are most people unfamiliar with caecilians? **Caecilians spend most of their time underground and live only in tropical rain forests, so most people never see them.**

LESSON 15

AMPHIBIAN METAMORPHOSIS

MAKING A CHANGE

SUPPLY LIST

Copy of "Amphibian Lifecycle" worksheet   Tadpoles (optional)   Tank   Food for raising a frog

BEGINNERS

- What is a baby frog called? **A tadpole.**
- What does a tadpole look like? **Like a little fish.**
- How does a tadpole change as it grows? **It grows legs, loses its tail, and grows lungs.**

AMPHIBIAN LIFECYCLE WORKSHEET

- **See illustrations in student manual, page 64.**

WHAT DID WE LEARN?

- Describe the stages an amphibian goes through in its lifecycle. **It begins as an egg, and then it hatches into a larva. In a frog, this is the tadpole stage. Then, it slowly changes into an adult. This is the metamorphosis stage in which lungs develop and gills disappear, and the creature changes its shape from a water dweller without legs to a land dweller with legs.**
- What are gills? **They are special organs on the sides of water animals that extract oxygen from the water as water passes over or through them.**
- What are lungs? **They are special organs that extract oxygen from the air as air passes through them.**

TAKING IT FURTHER

- Does the amphibian lifecycle represent molecules-to-man evolution? Why or why not? **NO! Evolution says that one kind of animal changes into another. A frog is still a frog even when it is a tadpole. A tadpole always changes into a frog. It does not grow up to be a bird or a mammal or even a salamander. It is always what God made it to be, even if its infant form is significantly different from its adult form.**

LESSON 16 REPTILES

SCALY ANIMALS

SUPPLY LIST

Paper   Pictures of reptiles   Sequins or flat beads   Glue

BEGINNERS

- Name three different kinds of reptiles. **Lizards, snakes, turtles, crocodiles, and alligators.**
- What do reptiles have covering their skin? **Scales.**
- Where do reptiles live? **In all parts of the world.**

WHAT DID WE LEARN?

- What makes reptiles different from amphibians? **Reptiles have scales and amphibians do not. Also, reptiles have lungs all their lives and do not go through metamorphosis.**
- What are the four groups of reptiles? **Lizards, snakes, turtles, and crocodiles.**

Taking it further

- How do reptiles keep from overheating? **They stay in the shade or other cooler places during the hottest part of the day. Many sleep during the day and are only active at night.**

- What would a reptile likely do if you dug it out of its winter hibernation spot? **It would appear dead. It would not move or eat. If you brought it inside and it warmed up, then it would seem to come alive, though it is actually alive even in its hibernating state.**

LESSON
17 SNAKES

THOSE HISSING, SLITHERING CREATURES

SUPPLY LIST

An open area on the floor for moving about

BEGINNERS

- What does a snake look like? **It is long and round with no legs and eyes on the side of its head.**

- How can a snake eat something bigger around than itself? **It can unhook its jaw and stretch its mouth around the prey.**

- Name three kinds of snakes. **Bull, rat, garter, python, boa, rattlesnake, coral, and cobra.**

WHAT DID WE LEARN?

- How are snakes different from other reptiles? **They have no legs.**

- What are the three groups of snakes? **Constrictors, colubrids, and venomous snakes.**

- How is a snake's sense of smell different from that of most other animals? **It uses its tongue to collect scent particles, and then touches them to an organ called the Jacobson's organ inside its mouth.**

- What is unique about how a snake eats? **It swallows its food whole and can eat something larger than its body diameter by unhooking its jaw and stretching its mouth very wide.**

TAKING IT FURTHER

- How are small snakes different from worms? **Snakes have backbones, scales, and well-developed eyes. Worms do not have any of these. Also, snakes have much more complicated internal systems.**

- If you see a snake in your yard, how do you know if it is dangerous? **You should learn to identify snakes using a guidebook or other resource. Unless you have your parent's permission, you should never approach a snake.**

LESSON 18 LIZARDS

CHAMELEONS AND GILA MONSTERS

SUPPLY LIST

Paper   Markers, colored pencils or paints   Face paint

BEGINNERS

- What common body parts do all lizards have? **Long thin bodies, tapered tails, feet with claws, and scales.**
- What do most lizards eat? **Insects.**
- How does a chameleon protect itself from its enemies? **It changes color to match its surroundings.**

WHAT DID WE LEARN?

- List three ways a lizard might protect itself from a predator. **It could change its color, crawl into a crack in a rock and inflate its body, or break off its tail to escape.**
- What do lizards eat? **Mostly insects; some eat plants and others eat dead animals.**

TAKING IT FURTHER

- Horny lizards are short compared to many other lizards and are often called horny toads. What distinguishes a lizard from a toad? **Lizards are reptiles, toads are amphibians. Toads do not have scales but lizards do. Also, lizards do not have gills when they are young, nor do they experience metamorphosis, but toads do.**
- Why might some people like having lizards around? **They eat insects and do not harm people.**
- How does changing color protect a lizard? **It makes it hard for the predator to see it.**
- What other reasons might cause a lizard to change colors? **To attract a mate or scare off competitors.**

LESSON 19 TURTLES & CROCODILES

TURTLE OR TORTOISE, CROCODILE OR ALLIGATOR— HOW DO YOU TELL?

SUPPLY LIST

Copy of "How Can You Tell Them Apart?" worksheet   Sink   Tape (cloth or first aid tape is best)

BEGINNERS

- What do turtles have that no other reptiles have? **A shell.**
- Where do tortoises usually live? **On land.**
- What are the largest reptiles? **Crocodiles and alligators.**
- How do crocodiles often catch their prey? **They float in the water and look like logs waiting for an animal to come near the edge of the water.**

How Can You Tell Them Apart? worksheet

- **Student drawings should be similar to pictures in student manual, page 81.**

What did we learn?

- Where do turtles usually live? **In the water.**
- Where do tortoises usually live? **On land.**
- How does the mother crocodile carry her eggs to the water? **In her mouth.**
- Why can't you take a turtle out of its shell? **Its shell is part of its body.**
- How do crocodiles stalk their prey? **They float in the water, wait for prey to approach and then clamp their jaws around the prey and drag it under the water to drown it before eating it.**

Taking it further

- Why might it be difficult to see a crocodile? **When it is floating in the water, it looks very much like a fallen log. This is how it tricks its prey into coming close enough to be eaten.**

QUIZ 3

Amphibians & Reptiles

Lessons 14–19

1. What defines an animal as a vertebrate? **Vertebrates have backbones with a spine along the back ending in a brain.**

Place the letters of the characteristics that apply next to each animal group.

2. Mammals: **A, C, G, J, L, (H for some)**
3. Birds: **A, E, H, J, M**
4. Fish: **B, D, H, K N, (G for a few)**
5. Reptiles: **B, D, H, J**
6. Amphibians: **B, F, H I , J, K**

Challenge questions

Fill in the blank with the correct term from below.

7. Amphibians communicate primarily by _**sound**_.
8. Male frogs have inflatable _**air sacs**_ for communication.
9. Each frog species communicates on a different _**frequency**_.
10. The Surinam toad presses eggs into the mother's _**back**_.
11. The midwife toad carries eggs strapped to its _**legs**_.
12. The mouth brooding frog carries its tadpoles in its _**mouth/air sacs**_.
13. A _**triceratops**_ is a ceratopian dinosaur.
14. An _**allosaurus**_ is a theropod dinosaur.
15. An _**apatosaurus**_ is a sauropod dinosaur.
16. Marine iguanas are well adapted to life in and near the _**water**_.
17. The _**carapace**_ is the top part of the turtle's shell.
18. The _**plastron**_ is the bottom part of the turtle's shell.

UNIT 4
ARTHROPODS

LESSON 20

INVERTEBRATES

CREATURES WITHOUT A BACKBONE

SUPPLY LIST

A good imagination   White board with markers (optional)

BEGINNERS

- What is an invertebrate? **An animal without a backbone.**
- Are invertebrates usually big or small animals? **Usually small animals.**
- Where do invertebrates live? **Everywhere on the earth.**

WHAT DID WE LEARN?

- What are some differences between vertebrates and invertebrates? **The main difference is that vertebrates have backbones that protect their spinal cords. Invertebrates do not have backbones or spinal cords. Also, vertebrates have internal skeletons and invertebrates don't.**
- What are the six categories of invertebrates? **Arthropods, mollusks, cnidarians, echinoderms, sponges, and worms.**

TAKING IT FURTHER

- Why might we think that there are more vertebrates than invertebrates in the world? **We don't notice invertebrates as much as we do vertebrates. Invertebrates are usually small, a great many are microscopic, and so we just don't see them as often. Also, many invertebrates live in the water, so, again, we don't see them very often.**

LESSON 21

ARTHROPODS

INVERTEBRATES WITH JOINTED FEET

SUPPLY LIST

Copy of the "Arthropod Pie Chart"
Supplies for Challenge: Balloons   Newspaper   String   Flour

BEGINNERS

- What is the same about the bodies of all arthropods? **They have jointed feet, they have more than one body section, and they do not have bones but do have an outer coating.**

- What is the biggest group of arthropods? **Insects.**

- What is the second biggest group of arthropods? **Spiders.**

ARTHROPOD PIE CHART

_A_ Insects   _C_ Crustaceans   _B_ Arachnids   _E_ Centipedes   _D_ Millipedes

WHAT DID WE LEARN?

- What do all arthropods have in common? **They are invertebrates [no backbone] with jointed feet, segmented bodies, and exoskeletons.**

- What is the largest group of arthropods? **Insects, with over 1 million species.**

TAKING IT FURTHER

- How are endoskeletons (internal) and exoskeletons (external) similar? **They both provide support and protection for the body. They help give the animal its form and shape.**

- How are endoskeletons and exoskeletons different? **Endoskeletons are on the inside of the body and are usually made of bone or cartilage. Also, endoskeletons grow as the body grows. Exoskeletons are on the outside of the body and are made from chitin, a substance similar to starch. Exoskeletons do not grow with the animal and must be shed and replaced periodically as the body grows.**

- Why should you be cautious when hunting for arthropods? **Many arthropods are poisonous, including some spiders, scorpions, and centipedes.**

LESSON 22

INSECTS

DON'T LET THEM BUG YOU.

SUPPLY LIST

Copy of "Water Skipper Pattern"   Paint   Bowl of water   3 Styrofoam balls per child
4 pipe cleaners per child   1 index card per child   Scissors   2 toothpicks per child
Paper   Tape

BEGINNERS

- How many body parts do insects have? **Three.**

- How many legs do insects have? **Six.**

- Name three common insects. **Butterflies, mosquitoes, flies, bees, beetles, moths, crickets, and grasshoppers.**

WHAT DID WE LEARN?

- What characteristics classify an animal as an insect? **Insects are invertebrates with jointed feet, 3 body parts [head, thorax, and abdomen], 6 legs, antennae, and usually havie wings.**

- How can insects be harmful to humans? **They can destroy crops and spread disease.**

- How can insects be helpful? **Some insects eat other insects. For example, dragonflies eat mosquitoes, and ladybugs eat aphids. Many insects pollinate flowers. Other insects provide food for many other animals.**

TAKING IT FURTHER

- How might insects make noise? **Some insects make noise by flapping their wings. Others, like crickets, rub their legs together to make noises.**

LESSON 23

INSECT METAMORPHOSIS

MAKING A CHANGE

SUPPLY LIST

Copy of "Stages of Metamorphosis" worksheet   Sleeping bag   2 scarves or other pieces of cloth
Butterfly larvae and habitat (optional)

BEGINNERS

- What are the three stages of a grasshopper's life? **Egg, nymph, and adult.**
- What are the four stages of a butterfly's life? **Egg, larva, chrysalis, and adult.**

STAGES OF METAMORPHOSIS WORKSHEET

- **See student manual, page 96.**

WHAT DID WE LEARN?

- What are the three stages of incomplete metamorphosis? **Egg, nymph, and adult.**
- What are the four stages of complete metamorphosis? **Egg, larva, chrysalis (or pupa), and adult.**

TAKING IT FURTHER

- What must an adult insect look for when trying to find a place to lay her eggs? **The eggs must be laid on a plant that the larva can eat. A larva spends most of its time eating and cannot search for food, so food must be readily available.**

LESSON 24

ARACHNIDS

SPIDERS AND SUCH

SUPPLY LIST

Several large and small marshmallows for each child   1 toothpick per child
Flexible wire (about 4 inches for each child)   4–6 pipe cleaners per child

Optional: 2 round crackers per child   Peanut butter   2 raisins per child   Spider webs
8 pretzel sticks per child   Powdered sugar   Magnifying glass

BEGINNERS

- How many legs does a spider have? **Eight.**
- How many body parts does a spider have? **Two.**
- What do insects have as part of their bodies that spiders do not have? **Wings and antennae.**
- Why does a spider spin a web? **To catch insects to eat.**

WHAT DID WE LEARN?

- How do arachnids differ from insects? **Arachnids have only two body parts (cephalothorax and abdomen), eight legs, no wings or antennae, and many spin webs.**
- Why are ticks and mites called parasites? **They feed off of living hosts.**

TAKING IT FURTHER

- Why don't spiders get caught in their own webs? **Only some of the web strands are sticky. The spider walks on the ones that are not sticky. Also, spiders secrete an oily substance that coats their feet and keeps them from sticking to their own webs.**

LESSON
25 CRUSTACEANS
ARE THEY CRUSTY?

SUPPLY LIST

Modeling clay   Magnifying glass for optional activity
Supplies for Challenge: Research materials on crustaceans

BEGINNERS

- Name three crustaceans. **Crab, lobster, shrimp, crayfish, and roly-poly.**
- How many body parts does a crustacean have? **Two.**
- Why is the crayfish's mouth on the underneath side of its body? **Because it eats food from the bottom of the riverbed.**

WHAT DID WE LEARN?

- What do all crustaceans have in common? **They have jointed legs, exoskeletons, two body sections, two pairs of antennae, and two or more pairs of legs and gills.**
- What are some ways that the crayfish is specially designed for its environment? **It has claws for defense and for eating. Its mouth is on the underside of its body, making it easier to eat food from the bottom of the river.**

TAKING IT FURTHER

- Why might darting backward be a good defense for the crayfish? **It is unexpected and can confuse an enemy.**

- At first glance, scorpions and crayfish (or crawdads) look a lot alike. How does a scorpion differ from a crayfish? **A scorpion lives on land and has eight legs, a stinger, and no antennae. Crayfish live in the water and have ten legs, antennae, and no stingers.**

- How can something as large as a blue whale survive by eating only tiny crustaceans? **It eats lots and lots of them—up to 8,000 pounds (3600 kg) per day!**

- If you want to observe crustaceans, what equipment might you need? **Jar, net, microscope or magnifying glass, and a trap.**

MYRIAPODS

HOW MANY SHOES WOULD A CENTIPEDE HAVE TO BUY?

SUPPLY LIST

A good memory and a sense of adventure   (A baseball cap might be fun, too.)
Supplies for Challenge: Modeling clay   Pipe cleaners or craft wire

BEGINNERS

- What does myriapod mean? **Many feet.**
- Which myriapod has poisonous claws? **Centipede.**
- How can you tell a centipede from a millipede? **Centipedes have flat bodies and only one set of legs on each body segment, millipedes have round bodies and two sets of legs on each body segment.**

WHAT DID WE LEARN?

- How can you tell a centipede from a millipede? **Centipedes are usually smaller, flatter and have longer antennae. Also, centipedes have 1 pair of legs per body segment while millipedes have 2 pairs per segment.**
- What are the 5 groups of arthropods? **Insects, arachnids, crustaceans, centipedes, and millipedes.**
- What do all arthropods have in common? **They have jointed legs, exoskeletons, and 2 or more body regions.**

TAKING IT FURTHER

- What are some common places you might find arthropods? **Nearly everywhere!**
- Arthropods are supposed to live outside, but sometimes they get into our homes. What arthropods have you seen in your home? **Ants, flies, mosquitoes, spiders, etc..**

QUIZ 4

ARTHROPODS

LESSONS 20–26

Write Yes if the creature below is an arthropod, write No if it is not.

1. _**Yes**_ ant
2. _**Yes**_ tick
3. _**No**_ trout
4. _**Yes**_ spider
5. _**Yes**_ scorpion
6. _**Yes**_ crab
7. _**Yes**_ cricket
8. _**Yes**_ butterfly
9. _**No**_ clam
10. _**No**_ mouse
11. _**Yes**_ centipede
12. _**No**_ snail
13. _**Yes**_ roly-poly
14. _**Yes**_ crawdad
15. _**No**_ starfish
16. _**No**_ lizard

17. What are the four stages of complete metamorphosis for an insect? **egg**, **larva**, **chrysalis (or pupa)**, **adult**

Fill in the blanks with the appropriate numbers.

18. An insect has _**3**_ body parts, _**6**_ legs, _**2**_ antennae and _**2 or 4**_ wings.

19. A spider has _**2**_ body parts, _**8**_ legs, _**0**_ antennae and _**0**_ wings.

20. A centipede has _**1**_ pair(s) of legs per body segment and a millipede has _**2**_ pair(s) of legs per body segment.

CHALLENGE QUESTIONS

Short answer:

21. Explain the purpose of an arthropod's exoskeleton. **The exoskeleton provides protection, keeps the animal from drying out, gives it form.**

22. What is the main ingredient in an exoskeleton? **Starch or chitin.**

23. Identify which segment (head, thorax, abdomen) is primarily responsible for each of the following functions in insects.

    Locomotion: **Thorax**   Internal functions: **Abdomen**   Sensory input: **Head**

24. What are two purposes of bioluminescence in fireflies? **Protection from enemies, finding a mate.**

25. Do male or female tarantulas live longer? **Female.**

26. What do tarantulas usually eat? **Grasshoppers, crickets, and other small animals.**

27. Name one interesting thing you learned about krill **Answers will vary**.

28. Name one interesting thing you learned about cleaner shrimp **Answers will vary.**

29. Name one interesting thing you learned about plankton **Answers will vary**.

30. Which is more dangerous, a centipede or a millipede? **Centipede is poisonous.**

OTHER INVERTEBRATES

LESSON 27 — MOLLUSKS

CREATURES WITH SHELLS

WORLD OF ANIMALS

SUPPLY LIST

Several sea shells   Shell identification guide
Supplies for Challenge: Balloon

BEGINNERS

- What kinds of mollusks have two-piece shells? **Clams and oysters.**

- Name a kind of mollusk that has a one-piece shell. **Snail.**

- How does a squid move through the water? **It squirts water out the back.**

- Which is considered the most intelligent mollusk? **The octopus.**

WHAT DID WE LEARN?

- What are three groups of mollusks? **Bivalves, gastropods, and cephalopods.**

- What body structures do all mollusks have? **They all have soft bodies, a muscular foot, a hump for internal organs and a mantle that forms a shell in most species.**

- How can you use a shell to help identify an animal? **The size, shape and coloring of each shell are unique to its species. Some shells spiral counter-clockwise and others spiral clockwise. Some are two pieces and some are only one piece.**

TAKING IT FURTHER

- How are pearls formed? **Any irritant that gets inside an oyster's shell is coated with a pearly substance over and over again. After a period of several years, it is large enough to be of value to people. To speed up this process, many oyster farmers now "seed" oysters by placing hard round objects that are nearly the size of a pearl inside oyster shells. After only a few months, these artificial pearls are ready for harvesting.**

LESSON 28

CNIDARIANS

JELLYFISH, CORAL, AND SEA ANEMONES

SUPPLY LIST

Paper   Modeling clay   Marshmallows   Pretzel sticks   Pictures of a coral reef
Whatever other craft supplies you have on hand
Supplies for Challenge: Live hydra specimens (Optional—can be ordered from a science supply store)

BEGINNERS

- Why do most fish try to stay away from jellyfish? **Jellyfish have poisonous stinging tentacles.**

- How does a coral protect itself? **It builds a crusty shell around itself.**

- What animal is related to coral and jellyfish? **Sea anemone.**

WHAT DID WE LEARN?

- What characteristics do all cnidarians share? **They have hollow bodies with stinging tentacles.**

- What are the three most common cnidarians? **Jellyfish, corals, and sea anemones.**

TAKING IT FURTHER

- How do you think some creatures are able to live closely with jellyfish? Accept reasonable answers. **Some animals have a tough skin or exoskeleton that protects them from jellyfish stings. Others have a special coating on their skin that protects them.**

- Why do you think an adult jellyfish is called a medusa? **The Medusa was a mythological creature with snakes for hair. A jellyfish, with all of its tentacles, resembles this creature.**

- Jellyfish and coral sometimes have symbiotic relationships with other creatures. What other symbiotic relationships can you name? **Some birds eat insects off of cattle. This feeds the birds and helps the cattle stay healthy. Also, lichen, that green and yellow scaly-looking substance on rocks, is actually fungus and algae living in a symbiotic relationship. The algae have chlorophyll and produce the food, while the fungus provides water, nutrients and protection. It is a beneficial relationship for both organisms.**

CHALLENGE: MAN O' WAR

- **Hydras can reproduce several different ways. They can reproduce by a process called budding where a new hydra forms from the side of the parent and then splits off. Hydras can also reproduce by sperm and eggs. Some species are able to produce both sperm and eggs from one animal. Other species have distinct male and female versions.**

LESSON 29

ECHINODERMS

SPINY-SKINNED CREATURES

SUPPLY LIST

Salt dough (1 cup salt, 1 cup flour, water to make a stiff dough)   Tag board or cardboard
Mini-chocolate chips
If possible: a real (dead) starfish or sand dollar (sometimes available at craft stores)
Supplies for Challenge (optional): A preserved starfish for dissection   Plastic gloves
Dissecting tray and scalpel

BEGINNERS

- How many legs does a starfish have? **Five.**
- What is a starfish's skin like? **Covered with spikes.**
- What amazing abilities does the starfish have? **It can push its stomach out through its mouth to digest an animal still in its shell and it can regenerated up to half of its body.**

WHAT DID WE LEARN?

- What are three common echinoderms? **Starfish (sea stars), sand dollars, and sea urchins.**
- What do echinoderms have in common? **They all have spiky skin and most have 5 body parts radiating from a central disk.**

TAKING IT FURTHER

- Why would oyster and clam fishermen not want starfish in their oyster and clam beds? **Starfish can eat up to a dozen clams or oysters a day. This hurts the fishermen's business.**
- What would happen if the fishermen caught and cut up the starfish and then threw them back? **The starfish would regenerate resulting in more starfish. This happened in one fishing village. The fishermen thought they were getting rid of the starfish by cutting them in half, but actually ended up making many more of them.**
- What purpose might the spikes serve on echinoderms? **Most spikes are used for protection from predators.**

LESSON 30

SPONGES

HOW MUCH WATER CAN A SPONGE HOLD?

SUPPLY LIST

Paper   Tempera paints   Synthetic sponges (and if possible, a real sea sponge)   Scissors

BEGINNERS

- What does a sponge have all through its body? **Holes.**
- What happens to a sponge when you cut it in half? **Each piece grows into a new sponge.**

WHAT DID WE LEARN?

- How does a sponge eat? **Nutrients are absorbed from the water as it passes through the body of the sponge.**
- How does a sponge reproduce? **A sponge can reproduce by releasing eggs or a sponge can regenerate to form new sponges from pieces that are cut or broken off of the original sponge.**
- Why is a sponge an animal and not a plant? **A sponge cannot produce its own food and it reproduces with eggs so it is an animal.**

TAKING IT FURTHER

- Why can a sponge kill a coral colony? **It is immune to the poison darts of the coral.**
- What uses are there for sponges? **They are sometimes used for cleaning. But mostly they are used for sponge painting and other artwork.**
- Why are synthetic sponges more popular than real sponges? **They are much less expensive.**

LESSON
31

WORMS

CREEPY CRAWLERS

SUPPLY LIST

Gummy worms   Dirt   Dried leaves   Rocks   Crushed chocolate cookies
Instant chocolate pudding
Supplies for Challenge: Paper   Paint   Drawing materials

BEGINNERS

- What do earthworms look like? **Long, thin, round, with rings around their bodies.**
- What do earthworms eat? **Dead plant material.**
- Why are earthworms helpful? **They turn the dead plants into fertilizer for new plants.**
- Name two kinds of worms other than earthworms. **Flat and round worms.**

WHAT DID WE LEARN?

- What kinds of worms are beneficial to man? **Segmented worms such as earthworms.**
- How are they beneficial? **They break down dead plant material, and can be used as fishing bait.**
- What kinds of worms are harmful? **Most other kinds of worms are parasitic and thus are harmful to their hosts; whether they are human or animal hosts.**

TAKING IT FURTHER

- How can you avoid parasitic worms? **Parasitic worms thrive in unsanitary conditions and are much more of a threat in undeveloped countries. Washing hands and raw vegetables and cooking meat well will help you avoid most parasites.**

QUIZ 5 — OTHER INVERTEBRATES
LESSONS 27–31

Mark each statement as either True or False.

1. _F_ All mollusks have visible shells.
2. _T_ A bivalve has two parts to its shell.
3. _T_ You can identify a mollusk by the shape of its shell.
4. _F_ The octopus is considered one of the least intelligent invertebrates.
5. _T_ Cnidarians usually experience a polyp stage sometime in their lifecycle.
6. _T_ Coral and algae have a symbiotic relationship.
7. _F_ Echinoderms are usually very dark colors.
8. _T_ Several invertebrates have the ability to regenerate.
9. _F_ Echinoderms have smooth skin.
10. _T_ A sponge is one of the simplest invertebrates.
11. _T_ Sponges can reproduce by eggs.
12. _F_ All worms are harmful to humans.

Short answer:

13. What do jellyfish, coral and sea anemones have in common? **They all have hollow bodies and stinging tentacles at least during part of their lifecycles.**
14. Name three groups of worms. **Segmented, flat, round.**
15. What part of the mollusk secretes its shell? **Mantle.**
16. Which kind of mollusk has only one part to its shell? **Gastropod.**
17. What is an adult jellyfish called? **Medusa.**
18. What is the name of the fertilizer produced by earthworms? **Compost.**

CHALLENGE QUESTIONS

Short answer:

19. Explain how cephalopods move. **Jet propulsion—suck in water then force it out the back.**
20. How can a nautilus remain buoyant as its shell gets bigger and heavier? **It fills inner chambers with gas/air.**
21. What is a siphonophore? **A collection of cnidarians living together in a symbiotic relationship.**
22. Name a common siphonophore. **Portuguese Man-of-War, by-the-wind sailor.**
23. What is a sieve plate in a starfish? **The openings that allow water into the starfish's water vascular system.**
24. What technology is being improved by the study of the Venus Flower Basket sponge? **Fiber optics.**
25. What is the name of the process that provides food for tubeworms? **Chemosynthesis.**

SIMPLE ORGANISMS

LESSON 32

KINGDOM PROTISTA

SIMPLE CREATURES?

SUPPLY LIST

Construction paper   Yarn   Shoe   Scissors   Glue   Colored pencils, markers, or crayons
Optional: Microscope   Pond water   Slides

BEGINNERS

- What are single-celled creatures called? **Protists.**
- How does a euglena move? **It has a tail that spins like a motor.**
- How does an amoeba move? **It pushes its body out like a finger then moves into that space.**
- How does a paramecium move? **It waves the hairs that cover its cell.**

WHAT DID WE LEARN?

- How are protists different from animals? **They consist of only one cell. Some contain chlorophyll.**
- How are they the same? **Protists reproduce, eat, move, grow and need oxygen just like other animals. Also, protists have all the same cell parts as other animal cells.**

TAKING IT FURTHER

- Why is a euglena a puzzle to scientists? **It has plant and animal characteristics.**
- Why are single-celled creatures not as simple as you might expect? **Just because there is only one cell does not mean it is simple. Single-celled creatures perform very complex functions. Most protists are more complex than any cell in the human body because human cells are more specialized and protist cells must perform more functions. Even the smallest organism demonstrates God's marvelous powers of design, and refutes the idea that life evolved on its own.**

LESSON 33

KINGDOM MONERA & VIRUSES

GOOD AND BAD GERMS

SUPPLY LIST

Hand soap and other anti-bacterial items in your house

BEGINNERS

- What are two types of germs? **Bacteria and viruses.**
- How can bacteria be helpful? **They break down dead plants and animals, they help with digestion.**

WHAT DID WE LEARN?

- How are bacteria similar to plants and animals? **They have cells, reproduce, and some can produce their own food.**
- How are bacteria different from plant and animal cells? **They do not have a defined nucleus.**
- How are viruses similar to plants and animals? **They have genetic information—DNA.**
- How are viruses different? **They do not reproduce on their own. They do not eat or grow in a normal sort of way.**

TAKING IT FURTHER

- Answer the following questions to test if a virus is alive.

  Does it have cells? **No.**

  Can it reproduce? **Only with the help of a host cell .**

  Is it growing? **Can't tell, they are too small to see even with an electron microscope.**

  Does it move or respond to its environment? **Yes**.

  Does it need food and water? **It needs host cells that use food and water. It is unclear if the viruses use these things directly.**

  Does it have respiration? **No.**

  Is it alive? **No, it does not have all of the requirements for biological life.**

- How can use of antibiotics be bad? **Antibiotics kill bacteria, but they cannot distinguish between good and bad bacteria. Overuse of antibiotics can kill too many of the good bacteria in your intestines and cause problems. Also, antibiotics kill most of the bad bacteria but some are resistant and do not die. These bacteria are the ones that survive and reproduce. The next generation of bacteria is not as easily killed by the antibiotics. Doctors are beginning to see diseases that used to respond to certain antibiotics no longer respond and must now be treated with stronger medicines. So we need to carefully use antibiotics when necessary, but not overuse them or use them incorrectly.**

QUIZ 6
SIMPLE ORGANISMS
LESSONS 32–33

Match the parts of a cell to its function.

1. _E_ Nucleus
2. _C_ Cell membrane
3. _B_ Cytoplasm
4. _A_ Mitochondria
5. _D_ Vacuole

Match the single-celled organism with its description.

6. _C_ Flagellate

7. _A_ Sarcodine

8. _B_ Ciliate

9. _E_ Bacteria

10. _D_ Virus

CHALLENGE QUESTIONS

Mark each statement as either True or False.

11. _F_ Sporozoans have a very simple lifecycle.

12. _T_ Sporozoans reproduce asexually and sexually.

13. _T_ Sporozoans are parasites.

14. _T_ Plasmodium is a dangerous protist.

15. _F_ Antibiotic-resistant bacteria prove evolution.

16. _F_ Survival of the fittest is the same as evolution.

17. _T_ Fossilized bacteria are very similar to modern bacteria.

18. _T_ Bacteria support biblical creation.

LESSON

34

ANIMAL NOTEBOOK

PUTTING THE ANIMALS TOGETHER

FINAL PROJECT SUPPLY LIST

Paper   Art supplies   Clip-art or other animal pictures   Worksheets from previous lessons
Photographs of projects from previous lessons

WHAT DID WE LEARN?

- What do all animals have in common? **They are alive, they reproduce, they do not make their own food, they can move about during at least part of their life.**

- What is the difference between vertebrates and invertebrates? **Vertebrates have a backbone and invertebrates do not.**

- What sets protists apart from all the other animals? **They are single-celled creatures. Some, like the euglena, can make their own food.**

TAKING IT FURTHER

- What are some of the greatest or most interesting things you learned from your study of the world of animals? **Answers will vary.**

- What would you like to learn more about? **Check out books from the library to learn more.**

FINAL EXAM

WORLD OF ANIMALS

LESSONS 1–34

Match each animal group with its unique characteristic.

1. _D_ Mammals
2. _G_ Birds
3. _A_ Fish
4. _F_ Reptiles
5. _H_ Amphibians
6. _B_ Arthropods
7. _C_ Mollusks
8. _I_ Echinoderms
9. _J_ Cnidarians
10. _E_ Protists

Define the following terms.

11. Invertebrate: **Animal without a backbone.**
12. Vertebrate: **Animal with a backbone.**
13. Cold-blooded animal: **Cold-blooded animals cannot regulate their body temperature; it is the same as the surrounding temperature.**
14. Warm-blooded animal: **Warm-blooded animals regulate their body temperature to keep it the same regardless of the surrounding temperature.**
15. Moneran: **Monerans are bacteria. They are single-celled organisms without a nucleus.**

Describe how a bird's feet are suited for each task listed below.

16. Swimming in a lake: **Webbed feet for paddling.**
17. Perching in a tree: **Three toes facing forward, one toe facing backward for grasping tree branches.**
18. Hunting prey: **Sharp claws (or talons) for grasping prey.**

Short answer:

19. Describe how a bird is specially designed for flight. **Birds have hollow bones, air-foil shaped wings, contour feathers that point toward the back of the body, special flight feathers, a tail that works like a rudder, and very efficient respiratory and circulatory systems.**
20. Name the three body parts of an insect. **head, thorax, abdomen**
21. Name the two body parts of a spider. **cephalothorax, abdomen**

Mark each statement as either True or False.

22. _T_ Snakes have a special organ for sensing smell.
23. _T_ Cold-blooded animals do not need to eat as often as warm-blooded animals.
24. _F_ Turtles can safely be removed from their shells.
25. _T_ Cartilaginous fish do not have any bones.
26. _T_ Centipedes are arthropods.
27. _F_ All crustaceans live in the water.

28. _T_ Insects are the most common arthropod.

29. _T_ Some creatures can live closely with jellyfish.

30. _F_ The best way to kill a starfish is to cut it in half.

CHALLENGE QUESTIONS

Match the term with its definition.

31. _B_ Unguligrade

32. _D_ Digitigrade

33. _E_ Plantigrade

34. _A_ Rumen

35. _G_ Abomasum

36. _C_ Reticulum

37. _F_ Omasum

Mark each statement as either True or False.

38. _F_ Darwin's finches prove evolution.

39. _T_ Birds have very efficient respiratory systems.

40. _T_ Fish sense food by smelling the water.

41. _F_ Frogs often confuse one species' call for another.

42. _T_ The largest dinosaurs were the sauropods.

43. _T_ Marine iguanas live only in the Galapagos Islands.

44. _F_ The plastron is the top of a turtle's shell.

45. _T_ A turtle's shell is made of the same material as fingernails.

Short answer:

46. Exoskeletons are made from _chitin/starch_.

47. The legs of an insect are attached to the _thorax/middle_ section of its body.

48. Bioluminescence causes an animal to _glow_.

49. Tarantulas have barbed _hairs_ that they kick at their enemies.

50. A _nautilus, octopus, squid, cephalopod_ moves through the water using jet propulsion.

51. Biomimetics is the study of animals to apply designs to _human technology_.

52. Tubeworms live near _hydrothermal vents_.

53. Plasmodium causes the disease _malaria_.

54. _Antibiotics_ are used to treat bacterial infections.

55. The stomach of a _mosquito_ is needed to complete the sexual reproduction of the plasmodium sporozoan.

LESSON
35

CONCLUSION

REFLECTING ON THE WORLD OF ANIMALS

SUPPLY LIST

Bible   Paper and pencil

WORLD OF ANIMALS

THE HUMAN BODY

HUMAN BODY

UNIT 1
BODY OVERVIEW

LESSON 1
THE CREATION OF LIFE
GOD CREATED THEM MALE AND FEMALE

SUPPLY LIST

Paper   Colored pencils   Mirror   Bible

BEGINNERS

- How did God create the first man, Adam? **God created man from the dust of the ground and breathed life into him.**
- In whose image did God create man? **In God's own image.**

WHAT DID WE LEARN?

- On which day of creation did God make man? **On the sixth day.**
- In whose image did God create man? In **God's image.**
- According to Genesis 1:26, over what were man and woman to rule? **Fish, birds, livestock, all the earth, and all the creatures on the earth.**

TAKING IT FURTHER

- Since we are created in God's image, how should we treat our bodies? **We should take care of our bodies and keep them healthy.**

LESSON 2
OVERVIEW OF THE HUMAN BODY
WE ARE FEARFULLY AND WONDERFULLY MADE!

SUPPLY LIST

Copy of "Body Wheel" (do not copy back to back)   Crayons, colored pencils, or markers
Paper fasteners   Scissors

BEGINNERS

- What part of your body moves your blood? **Heart.**
- What parts of your body help you move? **Bones and muscles.**

- Who created all the special parts of the human body? **God.**

WHAT DID WE LEARN?

- Name as many of the body's systems as you can and describe what each system does. **Answers will vary.**

TAKING IT FURTHER

- Which body systems are used when you walk across a room? **All of them. Your nervous, skeletal and muscular systems help you move. But also, your circulatory system provides oxygen and nutrients to your muscles. Your respiratory and digestive systems are what give your blood the oxygen and nutrients. And finally, your skin is needed to protect you as you walk.**

LESSON 3

HUMAN CELLS, TISSUES, & ORGANS

THE BUILDING BLOCKS OF OUR BODIES

SUPPLY LIST

Copy of "Body Cells" worksheet

BEGINNERS

- What are the smallest parts of your body called? **Cells.**
- What do these parts make when they are put together? **Tissues and organs.**

BODY CELLS WORKSHEET

A. **Nerve cell**
B. **Muscle cell**
C. **White blood cell**
D. **Skin cell**
E. **Red blood cell**
F. **Bone cell**

WHAT DID WE LEARN?

- What is the function of each of the following kinds of cells: skin cells, red blood cells, white blood cells, bone cells, nerve cells, and muscle cells? **Skin cells provide protection to seal out harmful substances and seal in moisture. Red blood cells carry oxygen to and carbon dioxide away from all the cells of the body. White blood cells eliminate invading germs and other harmful substances. Bone cells provide strength. Nerve cells relay messages. Muscle cells contract and expand to allow movement.**

TAKING IT FURTHER

- How has God uniquely designed red blood cells to transport oxygen? **They are round and smooth so they easily flow through blood vessels. Also, their cell membranes allow oxygen and carbon dioxide to easily pass through.**
- How are nerve cells specially designed to carry signals? **They have long tendrils or finger-like projections allowing a few cells to cover a large distance in the body, and thus signals can travel very quickly.**
- How did God design skin cells to perform their special functions? **Their rectangular shape allows them to fit snuggly together making an effective wall against germs and preventing moisture loss in your body.**
- With all these cells working together, what do you think is the largest organ in the body? **You might guess the stomach, heart or brain, but your skin is actually the largest organ in your body.**

CHALLENGE: TISSUE TYPES

Skin: **Epithelial tissue**
Tendons: **Connective tissue**
Brain: **Nerve tissue**
Fat: **Connective tissue**

Muscles: **Muscle tissue**
Lining of the mouth: **Epithelial tissue**
Inside of lungs: **Epithelial tissue**
Bones: **Connective tissue**

QUIZ 1 — BODY OVERVIEW

LESSONS 1–3

Fill in the blanks with the correct term.

1. Many cells working together are called a _**tissue**_.
2. _ **Red blood** _ cells carry oxygen to the body.
3. _**Muscle**_ cells stretch and contract to allow for movement.
4. The _**cell membrane**_ acts like the skin of a cell.
5. The _**nucleus**_ is the brain or control center of a cell.
6. Vacuoles are where cells store _**food**_.
7. Mitochondria break down food to provide _**energy**_ for the cell.
8. Humans were created in _**God's**_ image.
9. The _**skeletal**_ system provides strength for the body.
10. _**Nerve**_ cells can be over a yard long.
11. Nutrients are provided to the body through the _**digestive**_ system.
12. _**Skin**_ protects the body from harmful substances outside the body.
13. _**Bone**_ cells have a criss-cross shape.
14. Several tissues working together are called an _**organ**_.
15. A system is made up of _**cells**, **tissues,**_ and _**organs**_ all working together to perform a specific function.

CHALLENGE QUESTIONS

Fill in the blanks with the correct term.

21. The _**endocrine**_ system produces chemical messengers to control body functions.
22. Waste products are removed from the body by the _**kidneys or excretory system** _.
23. A mother carries the unborn baby in her _**womb or uterus**_.
24. Bones are _**connective**_ tissue.
25. _**Epithelial**_ tissue covers the inside of your stomach.
26. Your brain is made up of _**nerve**_ tissue.

UNIT 2
BONES & MUSCLES

LESSON 4

THE SKELETAL SYSTEM

STRUCTURE AND STRENGTH

SUPPLY LIST

Copy of "Sandy Skeleton" (do not copy back to back)   Scissors   5 paper fasteners for each child
Supplies for Challenge: Tape measure

BEGINNERS

- What are three things that bones do for you? **They determine how tall and how wide you are; they give you strength; they help you move.**
- Do bones bend? **No, the joints between the bones allow the bones to move.**

WHAT DID WE LEARN?

- What are three jobs that bones perform? **They provide strength, produce blood cells, and store calcium for future use.**
- How are muscles connected to bones? **By cords called tendons.**
- What keeps bones from rubbing against each other at the joints? **A cushioning material called cartilage is between the bones.**
- How many bones does an adult human have? **206.**
- What is the main mineral in bones? **Calcium.**

TAKING IT FURTHER

- What do you think is the largest bone in the body? **The femur or large leg bone is the longest and largest bone in the body.**
- Why does this bone need to be so large? **The femur bones support most of the body's weight.**
- What do you think are the smallest bones in the body? **The three bones in the inner ear—the malleus, incus, and stapes—are the smallest bones.**

BONES & MUSCLES · 93

LESSON 5

NAMES OF BONES

WHAT'S A CLAVICLE?

SUPPLY LIST

Washable gel pens   Anatomy book
Supplies for Challenge: Anatomy book   Copy of "What's My Name?" worksheet

BEGINNERS

- How many bones do you have in your body? **206.**
- What is the bone on the top of your head called? **Skull.**
- What is the name of the bone that opens and closes your mouth? **Jawbone/mandible.**
- What is the name of the bone at the front of your knee? **Kneecap/patella.**
- What is the name of the long bone in the top of your leg? **Femur.**

WHAT DID WE LEARN?

- Review the names of the bones by pointing to each bone as you name it.
- Is your cranium above or below your mandible? **Your cranium, or skull, is above your mandible, which is your jaw bone. Of course, this is not true if you are standing on your head.**
- What is moving if you wiggle your phalanges? **Your fingers and your toes.**

TAKING IT FURTHER

- What happens if you cross your legs and gently hit just below your patella? **Your leg swings out with a reflex action. We will learn more about this when we study the nervous system.**
- Why do we have Latin names for body parts? **This allows scientists to communicate about the body even if they do not speak the same language. This is why many scientific terms, not just body parts, are in Latin.**

CHALLENGE: WHAT'S MY NAME? WORKSHEET

1. I hold your ribs together. **Sternum.**
2. Your collar rests on me. **Clavicle.**
3. Pat me on the back. **Scapula or vertebrae.**
4. I support your weight when you stand. **Femur.**
5. Listen, you might find us in a blacksmith shop. **Hammer, anvil, and stirrup.**
6. I'm in your leg, and that's no lie. **Fibula.**
7. I rotate around your wrist. **Radius.**
8. You wouldn't want to stub me. **Phalanges.**
9. Man, I talk a lot. **Mandible.**
10. When you cross your legs, I pop up. **Patella.**

TYPES OF BONES

ARE ALL BONES CREATED EQUAL?

SUPPLY LIST

Anatomy book   Model of Sandy Skeleton from lesson 4
Supplies for Challenge: 2 chicken leg or thigh bones   Vinegar   Cup

BEGINNERS

- What are three different shapes of bones in your body? **Short, long, flat, round, and unusual.**

WHAT DID WE LEARN?

- Which bones are designed mainly for protection of internal organs? **Flat bones such as your cranium and ribs.**
- Which type of bones helps determine what your face will look like? **Irregular bones in your face.**
- Which type of bones works closely with your circulatory system to replace old blood cells? **The long bones in your arms and legs.**

TAKING IT FURTHER

- Why are the long bones filled with marrow and not solid? **If they were solid, they would be too heavy to move easily. Also, the hollow design gives the bones more strength, since a cylinder is stronger than a solid rod. Finally, the marrow is where the red blood cells are produced.**
- What is the advantage of having so many small bones in your hands? **This allows you to be flexible and move your fingers in lots of different ways so you can scratch your back, pick up a baby or cook dinner.**

JOINTS

CONNECTIONS ARE IMPORTANT

SUPPLY LIST

Items found around your house
Supplies for Challenge: 2 wooden pencils   Tacks   Wide rubber bands

BEGINNERS

- What is a joint? **A place where two bones come together.**
- How does you knee joint move? **It swings back and forth.**
- How does your neck joint move? **Rotates from side to side and up and down.**

SCAVENGER HUNT

- door hinges: **Hinge.**
- sliding doors: **Gliding.**
- joints in pets: **Depends on the pet—dogs and cats have many of the same types of joints as humans including ball and socket, hinge, and others.**
- LEGO® pieces: **May be able to find ball and socket, pivot, or saddle joints.**
- nut crackers: **Hinge.**
- pliers: **Pivot.**

WHAT DID WE LEARN?

- What was the most common joint found around your house? **You probably found lots of hinges. This is the simplest kind of joint and is actually a modified lever and a very efficient way to move things.**

TAKING IT FURTHER

- Which came first, the joints in the body or the joints in your house? **Obviously, the body was created first. Man realized the beauty and usefulness of God's designs and used them in many of his own inventions.**
- Why do you need so many different kinds of joints in your body? **The different kinds of joints give our bodies lots of flexibility and strength, allowing us to move in so many different ways.**

LESSON 8

THE MUSCULAR SYSTEM

MAKING IT MOVE

SUPPLY LIST

Supplies for Challenge: Piece of raw steak or other meat   Magnifying glass

BEGINNERS

- What is the main job of your muscles? **To move your bones.**
- What are the names of the muscles in your upper arm? **Bicep and tricep.**
- What does your diaphragm muscle do? **It helps you breathe by expanding your chest.**

WHAT DID WE LEARN?

- How does a contracted muscle feel? **More rigid than a relaxed muscle.**
- How does a muscle get stretched? **After it relaxes, it is pulled by another muscle attached to the opposite side of a bone.**

TAKING IT FURTHER

- How does a muscle know when to contract? **The brain sends a message to it telling it to contract.**
- How does your face express emotion? **Your brain works together with your muscles to change the expression on your face. Muscles around your mouth and eyes move to show sadness, surprise, anger or happiness.**

LESSON 9

DIFFERENT TYPES OF MUSCLES

AREN'T THEY ALL THE SAME?

SUPPLY LIST

Yard stick   Stopwatch

BEGINNERS

- How can you make your muscles stronger? **By using them or exercising.**
- How do you make most muscles move? **By thinking about it.**
- What are some muscles that move without you having to think about it? **Your heart beats, your diaphragm moves your chest, and muscles move food through your digestive system.**

WHAT DID WE LEARN?

- What are the two types of muscles? **Voluntary and involuntary.**
- How can we keep our muscles healthy? **By eating healthy foods, exercising, and stretching before you begin exercising.**
- How do your muscles learn? **Your brain automates functions that you do over and over again.**
- What are some advantages of exercising? **Muscle strength, speed, endurance, and more energy.**

TAKING IT FURTHER

- Do you need to exercise your facial muscles? **Yes. Make funny faces at your mom**.

CHALLENGE: MUSCLE TISSUE

Diaphragm: **Striated**   Tongue: **Striated**   Esophagus: **Smooth**
Mother's womb: **Smooth**   Hand muscle: **Striated**   Heart: **Cardiac**

LESSON 10

HANDS & FEET

SPECIAL DESIGNS FROM GOD

SUPPLY LIST

Pencil   Paper   Cup
Supplies for Challenge: Anatomy book   Drawing materials

BEGINNERS

- What are some things that are special about the way that God designed your hands and feet? **They are very flexible, have friction skin, have nails for protection, and can help you do many things.**

What did we learn?

- Which is the most important finger? **The thumb.**
- Why is the thumb so important? **It is needed for grasping almost everything.**
- What are some special features God gave to hands and feet? **They have flexibility because of multiple joints, sensitivity because of a vast array of nerves, special gripping skin, and protective nails.**

Taking it further

- What activities or jobs require special use of the hands? **Musician, artist, and construction worker are just a few of the occupations requiring special use of the hands.**
- What jobs require special use of the feet? **Most athletes, for example soccer players and dancers.**

QUIZ 2 — BONES & MUSCLES

LESSONS 4–10

Place the letter for the correct bone type next to each description below.

1. _B_ Makes new blood cells
2. _A_ Found in hands and feet
3. _B_ Supports most of your weight
4. _B_ Found in arms and legs
5. _D_ Found in face
6. _C_ Gives protection to organs
7. _D_ Vertebrae
8. _A_ Gives flexibility in hands
9. _C_ Ribs and skull
10. _C_ Shoulder blades

Mark each statement as either True or False.

11. _F_ Muscles stretch and contract individually.
12. _T_ Muscles can be damaged by tearing.
13. _T_ Using muscles makes them stronger.
14. _T_ Approximately 40% of your body weight is from muscles.
15. _F_ What you eat does not affect your bones and muscles.

CHALLENGE QUESTIONS

Mark each statement as either True or False.

16. _T_ The arm and leg bones are part of the appendicular skeleton.
17. _F_ The axial skeleton primarily provides form and strength.
18. _T_ Blood clotting cells are some of the first cells at the site of a fracture.
19. _F_ Broken bones are usually weaker after they heal than before the break.
20. _T_ It can take weeks for a bone to fully heal.

21. _T_ Joints are designed to keeps bones in place and to move freely.
22. _T_ Individual muscles cells each contract to make a muscle contract.
23. _T_ Muscles help blood move through the body.
24. _F_ The heart is made up of skeletal muscle tissue.
25. _T_ Only hands and feet have friction skin.

Unit 3
Nerves & Senses

Lesson 11

The Nervous System

Telling your body what to do

Supply List

Copy of "Nervous System Coloring Page"   Stop watch   Ruler
Small object such as an eraser, pebble, or small toy

Beginners

- What is the name of the system that talks to the muscles in your body? **Nervous system.**
- What is the most important part of the nervous system? **The brain.**
- How do messages get from your brain to other parts of the body? **Through a system of nerves.**
- How do messages get from your body to your brain? **Through the same system of nerves.**

What did we learn?

- What are the three main parts of the nervous system? **Brain, spinal cord, and nerves.**
- In the response time test, what messages were sent to and from the brain? **The eye saw the object then released and sent that message to the brain. The brain then sent a message to the hand and arm muscles telling them to contract.**

Taking it further

- Name ways that information is collected by your body to be sent to the brain. **Eyes see, ears hear, your tongue tastes, your nose smells, and nerves in your skin send a variety of messages to your brain.**

Challenge: Unique Humans

- Make your own list of things that humans can do that animals cannot do. What accounts for each of these abilities? **Worship God—humans have a soul and animals do not, feel true emotions—this is a complex thing involving the nervous system and the soul.**

HUMAN BODY

THE BRAIN

CAPTAIN OF THE SHIP

SUPPLY LIST

3 different colors of modeling clay   Anatomy book

BEGINNERS

- Name some things that you do that use your brain. **Think, move, breathe, smell, see, hear, taste, and touch.**
- What are the three parts of the brain? **Cerebrum, cerebellum, and brain stem.**

WHAT DID WE LEARN?

- What are the three major parts of the brain? **Cerebrum, cerebellum, and brain stem.**
- Which part of the brain controls growth? **Pituitary gland.**

TAKING IT FURTHER

- Which part of the brain would be used for each of the following: running, dilating your eyes, learning your math facts? **The cerebellum controls muscles for running, the brain stem controls pupil dilation, and the cerebrum helps you learn new information like math facts.**
- Is your brain the same thing as your mind? **No, your brain helps you think but your mind is more than just your thinking ability. Your mind is who God has created you to be. It includes your personality, and your soul and spirit, which allow you to have a relationship with God. The human spirit is what truly sets man apart from the animals.**

CHALLENGE: BRAIN ANATOMY

- Thought: **Frontal lobe, front part of cerebrum.**
- Smell: **Sensory area, central part of cerebrum.**
- Heart beat regulation: **Medulla oblongata, part of brain stem.**
- Memory: **Memory center on side of cerebrum as well as hippocampus.**
- Sight: **Visual cortex, at back of cerebrum.**
- Speech: **Speech center behind frontal lobe.**
- Muscle control: **Motor area in center of cerebrum as well as cerebellum.**
- Pupil dilation: **Midbrain, part of the brain stem.**

HUMAN BODY

LESSON

13

LEARNING & THINKING

HOW DO YOU USE YOUR BRAIN?

SUPPLY LIST

6 index cards   6 different colored markers

BEGINNERS

- Are there any animals that can think and reason like people do? **No.**
- What part of your brain is used for thinking? **Cerebrum.**
- How can you make your brain stronger? **Exercise it—use it by reading, practicing math facts, and doing other things that require thought.**

WHAT DID WE LEARN?

- Which part of the brain does each of the following: stores short-term memories, stores long-term memories, controls learning and thinking, controls the senses? **Hippocampus—short-term memory, cerebral cortex—long-term memory, cerebrum—learning/thinking, senses.**
- Which side of the brain controls the left side of the body? **The right side.**
- What is necessary for a healthy brain? **Good nutrition, sleep, and mental exercise.**

TAKING IT FURTHER

- List ways you can learn something. **By hearing, feeling, seeing, doing, smelling, and tasting. You actually will remember something best if you see it, hear it, say it back, and then associate it with something else.**
- What is something you have trouble learning? **Come up with a new way to try to remember it. For example, if you have trouble remembering how to spell a word, write the letters you usually get wrong in a different color to help you see the right way to spell it.**

CHALLENGE: LOGIC PUZZLES

1. **The two 50 pound people go over together. One returns with the boat. One 100 pound person crosses over. The first 50 pound person returns with the boat. Again both 50 pounders cross over and one returns with the boat. The second 100 pound person crosses over. The second 50 pound person returns and picks up the first 50 pound person. This requires the boat to make 9 trips across the river.**
2. **Ask either person, "If I ask the other person which road leads to the nearest town what would he say?" If this is the person that tells the truth, he will tell you the lie the other person would say. If this person is the one that tells a lie, he will tell you a lie even though the other person would have told the truth. Either way, the answer you get will be the wrong road to take so you can take the other road.**

HUMAN BODY

LESSON 14

REFLEXES & NERVES

FASTER THAN LIGHTNING

SUPPLY LIST

2 sharp pencils or 2 toothpicks   Blindfold

Supplies for Challenge: Drawing materials   Research materials on multiple sclerosis

BEGINNERS

- What is in your skin that helps you feel things? **Nerves.**
- What allows you to move very quickly when you are in danger? **Reflexes.**

WHAT DID WE LEARN?

- How do reflex reactions differ from other nervous system messages? **They only go to the spinal cord not to the brain, so they are much faster.**
- Why do we have reflexes? **They help us avoid dangerous situations.**
- What are some different types of sensations detected by your nerves? **Texture, temperature, pain, vibration, and pressure.**

TAKING IT FURTHER

- What reflexes might you experience? **You duck if you sense something coming at you, close your eyes, or quickly pull back your hand when you touch something hot.**
- How does the sense of touch differ from your fingertips to the back of your arm? **More nerves on the fingers allow you to detect more subtle differences.**
- Why do you need a larger number of nerves on the bottoms of your feet? **To help you detect differences in the walking surface so you can keep your balance and not trip.**

LESSON 15

THE FIVE SENSES

LETTING YOUR BRAIN KNOW WHAT'S OUT THERE

SUPPLY LIST

3 bowls   Hot water   Warm water   Cold water   Sandwich bag filled with ice

Jacket with a zipper   2–3 straight pins

Supplies for Challenge: Glue   Paper

BEGINNERS

- What are your five senses? **Sight, hearing, smell, taste, and touch.**
- What are the parts of your body that provide these senses? **Eyes, ears, nose, tongue, and skin/nerves.**

- What parts of your body cannot feel anything? **Hair, fingernails, toenails.**

WHAT DID WE LEARN?

- What are your five senses? **Sight, hearing, taste, smell, and touch.**
- Which of these senses usually gives us the most information? **Sight.**
- How does your brain compensate for the loss of one of your senses? **Your brain uses the other senses more to gather missing information.**

TAKING IT FURTHER

- You have nerves all over your skin, so why don't you feel your clothes all day long? **Since the nerves detect the same feelings all day, your brain learns to ignore those messages so you don't notice your clothes. But if you really concentrate on it, you can feel your shirt rubbing against your arm.**
- Your eyes see your nose all day long. Why don't you notice it all the time? **Since your eyes see your nose in your peripheral vision all the time, your brain learns to ignore that image, and it disappears. If you really try, you can see your nose. Cover one eye, and it will be more obvious.**
- If you are in the hot sun for a while then you go inside, the room feels cold. Why? **Your brain is comparing the new temperature to the old temperature and decides it is cold. But after a few minutes, your brain becomes used to the new temperature and you don't feel cold anymore.**

CHALLENGE: BRAILLE SYSTEM

- **There are many more nerves in your fingertips than in the other parts of your hand, thus making it easier to feel differnt patterns of bumps.**

LESSON

16 THE EYE

WINDOW TO THE WORLD

SUPPLY LIST

Paper tube (such as a paper-towel roll or a rolled piece of paper)   Piece of paper
Supplies for Challenge: Anatomy book

BEGINNERS

- What are some parts of your eye that you can see when you look in the mirror? **Pupil, iris, white of your eye, eyelid, and eyelashes.**
- What is the purpose of the pupil? **Let light into the eye.**
- What is the purpose of the iris? **To make the pupil get bigger or smaller depending on the amount of light available.**
- What carries the picture from your eye to your brain? **Optic nerve.**

WHAT DID WE LEARN?

- Name four important parts of the eye. **Lens, pupil, iris, retina, rods and cones, and optic nerve.**
- How does your brain compensate for different amounts of light in your surroundings? **By opening and closing the pupil—contracting and relaxing the iris.**

- How does your brain help you to focus on items that are near and items that are far away? **By adjusting the shape of the lens—by contracting muscles in the eye.**
- Why did God design our bodies with two eyes instead of just one? **Two eyes at different positions give depth perception. Also, if one eye is damaged the other can compensate.**
- How does having two eyes help with a 3-dimensional image? **Each eye views an object from a different angle allowing you to see more of the sides and giving you a better idea of the whole object.**
- Since you have a blind spot, how can you see what is in that spot? **Your brain fills in with what is around the blind spot.**

TAKING IT FURTHER

- Name some ways that the eye is protected from harm. **Eyelids and eyelashes keep out debris, tears wash away debris, the pupil contracts in bright light, the skull protects the eyes from impact.**
- Why do some people have to wear glasses or contact lenses? **The brain adjusts the lenses in the eyes to bring images into focus. Some people have lenses that are too flat or too round to be changed enough to make the images focus properly. Eyeglasses or contact lenses help compensate for these misshapen lenses in the eyes.**
- Why can you fool your eyes or your brain into thinking you saw something you didn't actually see? **Your brain makes certain assumptions about what it expects to see based on what you normally see. If something is unusual you might be fooled, at least for a little while.**

CHALLENGE: LIQUID IN YOUR EYES

- Lens: **Changes shape to focus on an image.**
- Pupil: **Dilates or closes to control amount of light entering eye.**
- Iris: **Controls size of pupil.**
- Cornea: **Front of the eye - protects lens.**
- Rods: **Detect light.**
- Cones: **Detect color.**
- Retina: **Contains rods and cones, detects image.**
- Optic nerve: **Nerve that transmits image to the brain.**
- Vitreous humor: **Keeps eyeball firm.**
- Aqueous humor: **Keeps front of eye firm, supplies nutrients to front of eye.**

LESSON
17

THE EAR

DO YOU HEAR WHAT I HEAR?

SUPPLY LIST

Copy of "Do You Hear What I Hear?" worksheet

BEGINNERS

- Name three parts of your ear that are inside your head. **Eardrum, tiny bones, and auditory nerve.**
- How do people who cannot hear speak with other people? **Usually with sign language.**

Do You Hear What I Hear? worksheet

_A_ Steaming tea kettle   _D_ Violin   _C_ Man singing   _B_ Bass drum
_C_ Falling snow   _A_ A jet engine   _D_ A TV show   _B_ A whisper

What did we learn?

- What determines how high or low a sound will be? **The frequency or spacing of the waves determines the pitch.**

- What determines how loud or soft a sound will be? **The amplitude or height of the waves determines the volume.**

Taking it further

- Why do two different instruments playing the same note at the same loudness sound different? **A note played by an instrument is not one single pitch. It actually has the same note played at various intervals called harmonics. For example, a C on the piano will sound very different than a C on a trumpet because of the different harmonics that are generated by the instrument.**

- Name several ways to protect your hearing. **Ear plugs, ear phones, and turning down the volume.**

- How do you suppose deaf children learn to speak? **They watch other people to learn how to move their tongues, mouths and throats. They also can feel air movement from their mouths. Watch your mouth in a mirror as you say the sound of b and p. These sounds look the same. Then feel the air flow from your mouth as you say the same sounds. The p sound pushes out puffs of air but the b sound does not.**

- How do you think a CD player or a telephone makes sounds? **Electronic devices such as telephones and CD players take electrical signals and send them through a device that vibrates, causing the air to move and thus making sounds from the electrical signals. This is the opposite of how your ears work, since your ear takes vibrations and turns them into electrical signals.**

LESSON 18

Taste & Smell

What's for dinner?

Supply list

2–3 cotton swabs   Copy of "Tongue Map" worksheet   Potato   Apple   Carrot
Lemon juice (unsweetened)   Cocoa mixed with water   Sugar water   Salt water
Several spices or other items with familiar smells (cinnamon, peppermint, lemon juice, vinegar)

Beginners

- What are the four basic flavors? **Sweet, salty, sour, and bitter.**
- What sense works together with taste to give you the full flavor of food? **Smell.**

What did we learn?

- What four flavors can your tongue detect? **Salty, sweet, sour, and bitter.**
- How does your tongue detect flavors? **Bits of food dissolved in saliva touch different taste buds in your mouth, and the taste buds generate electrical signals that go to the brain.**

- How does your nose detect fragrances? **Scent particles enter your nasal cavity where smell-detecting nerves send signals to your brain.**

TAKING IT FURTHER

- Can you still taste foods when you have a stuffy nose? **Depending on how bad your cold is, you may or may not be able to smell the foods. If your nose is really stuffy, the foods may taste bland and you may lose some of your appetite.**

- Smells are used for more things than just enjoying food. List some other uses for your sense of smell. **Detecting dangerous odors such as smoke or gas, enjoying flowers, smelling the fresh air right after it rains.**

- Oranges and grapefruits are both sweet and sour. Why do they taste different? **They have different proportions of sweet to sour. Also, they have different fragrances. This gives them each a unique flavor.**

- Cocoa is very bitter. Why does chocolate candy taste so delicious? **The sweetness of the sugar combined with the bitterness makes it pleasant.**

CHALLENGE: HOW WE TASTE AND SMELL

- What is the input to each of your senses? **Sight—light/electromagnetic waves; sound—sound waves/ mechanical waves/vibrating air; touch—direct stimulation of nerves in the skin; taste—chemicals in food; smell—odorants, which are also chemicals in food or other items.**

QUIZ 3 NERVES & SENSES

LESSONS 11–18

1. Name the five senses your brain uses to collect information about the outside world.
   Sight   Hearing   Taste   Smell   Touch

Match each part of the brain with its function.

2. _D_ Cerebellum

3. _F_ Brain stem

4. _E_ Spinal cord

5. _C_ Cerebrum

6. _B_ Hippocampus

7. _A_ Pituitary gland

Mark each statement as either True or False.

8. _T_ You can improve your intelligence by exercising your brain.

9. _T_ Smells can bring back memories.

10. _F_ You don't need to wear a bike helmet when you ride your bike.

11. _F_ The left side of the brain controls the left side of the body.

12. _T_ What you eat affects your brain.

13. _F_ Reflexes are slower than normal signals to the brain.

14. _T_ Your brain fills in for the blind spot in your eye.

15. _T_ The louder the sound is the higher its amplitude.

CHALLENGE QUESTIONS

Choose the best answer for each question below.

16. _B_ Which nervous system is the only one capable of higher level complex thought?

17. _C_ Which neurons process and generate signals?

18. _A_ What is the function of myelin?

19. _D_ What liquid is found in the middle of the eye?

20. _C_ What part of the ear controls balance?

21. _A_ Which part of the tongue chemically reacts with food molecules?

22. _B_ What kind of molecules produce smells?

UNIT 4
DIGESTION

LESSON 19
THE DIGESTIVE SYSTEM
WHAT HAPPENS TO MY LUNCH?

SUPPLY LIST

Sandwich   Clock   Copy of "Where's My Lunch?" worksheet

Supplies for Challenge: Anatomy book   Copy of "Digestive System" worksheet

BEGINNERS

- What system of your body gets the energy out of the food you eat? **The digestive system.**
- Name three parts of your digestive system. **Mouth, teeth, tongue, stomach, small intestine, and large intestine.**
- How do food molecules get to all parts of your body? **They are absorbed into the blood then taken by the blood to all parts of the body.**

WHAT DID WE LEARN?

- What are the main parts of the digestive system? **Teeth, tongue, esophagus, stomach, small intestine, and large intestine.**
- What role do your teeth play in digestion? **They grind and chop your food into small enough pieces to swallow.**
- What role does your tongue play in digestion? **It helps move the food around in your mouth so you can chew it up, and it helps you swallow the food.**
- Which is longer, your small intestine or your large intestine? **Your small intestine.**
- Which is wider, your small intestine or your large intestine? **Your large intestine.**

TAKING IT FURTHER

- Can you eat or drink while standing on your head? **Yes. You may think that gravity pulls the food into your stomach, but that is not the case. Involuntary muscles inside your esophagus push the food down, so you can swallow even when you are upside down. You can test this by sipping some water through a straw while standing on your head. You may need some help to do this.**
- Why do some foods spend 1/2 hour in the stomach while other foods spend 3 hours in the stomach? **Foods that are high in fat or protein take longer to break down than foods that are mostly starches.**
- What makes you feel hungry? **When your stomach is empty, or nearly empty, it has nothing to move around, so it sends a message to your brain that you need more food. Only then do you feel hungry.**
- Why did God design your body with a way to make you feel hungry? **Because humans are warm-blooded, they need to have a fairly constant supply of energy to help maintain their body temperature. Also, eating regularly helps us to have the energy necessary to do all the activities we like to do.**

HUMAN BODY

DIGESTION · 109

CHALLENGE: DIGESTIVE SYSTEM WORKSHEET

1. _I_ Pancreas
2. _B_ Salivary glands
3. _A_ Tongue
4. _L_ Anus
5. _D_ Esophagus
6. _K_ Small intestine
7. _F_ Stomach
8. _E_ Liver
9. _G_ Gall bladder
10. _H_ Duodenum
11. _C_ Epiglottis
12. _J_ Large intestine

LESSON 20

TEETH

GRIND THAT FOOD

SUPPLY LIST

Tagboard, poster board, or other thick paper   Modeling clay   Plaster of Paris   Foil
Tape   Scissors   Small bowl or cup   Spoon
Supplies for Challenge: Three colors of modeling clay

BEGINNERS

- How do your teeth help with digestion? **You use them to chew up your food.**
- How many sets of teeth to do you have in your lifetime? **Two.**
- Why do you have more than one set of teeth? **Teeth do not grow as you grow bigger so smaller teeth are replaced with bigger teeth when you get bigger.**

WHAT DID WE LEARN?

- What is the job of each kind of tooth? **Incisors are for biting and cutting, canines are for tearing, and bicuspids and molars are for grinding.**
- Why do people have baby teeth and why do they fall out? **You need small teeth when your mouth is small. Teeth can't grow like the rest of your body so the small teeth fall out, making room for larger teeth as your mouth gets larger.**

TAKING IT FURTHER

- Why do we need to take care of our teeth? **If you don't take care of them, your teeth can get holes in them (cavities), break, or even fall out making it hard to eat and causing you pain.**

LESSON 21

DENTAL HEALTH

TAKING CARE OF THOSE TEETH

SUPPLY LIST

Toothbrush   Toothpaste   Dental floss   Mirror

Beginners

- How often should you brush your teeth? **At least twice a day.**
- Why should you go to the dentist regularly? **For better cleaning and to take care of cavities.**
- What can you do besides brushing to help keep your teeth healthy? **Floss, avoid sugary foods, and go to the dentist.**

What did we learn?

- What are three things you can do to have healthy teeth? **Brush regularly, floss regularly, eat healthy foods, and visit the dentist regularly.**
- How does brushing your teeth help keep them healthy? **Brushing removes plaque and reduces the likelihood of getting cavities.**
- List some foods that are good for your teeth. **Fruits, vegetables, and milk.**
- List some foods that are bad for your teeth. **Hard candy, sugary gum, and sipping sweet drinks for a long time.**

Taking it further

- Since your baby teeth are going to fall out anyway, why do you still need to brush them and take care of them? **You need to develop good habits even if you only have baby teeth. You will have a combination of baby and permanent teeth for several years. Also, even if your teeth are not damaged, bacteria can cause damage to the gums if you never clean your teeth.**

LESSON 22

Nutrition

What should you eat?

Supply list

Foods from all of the food groups (See food pyramid page 82 of student manual.)
Supplies for Challenge : Copy of "Nutrition" worksheet

Beginners

- What are the four groups of food mentioned in this lesson? **Grains, fruits and vegetables, milk and cheese (dairy), and meats.**
- Why do you need to eat some of each group every day? **Each group provides something different for your body.**
- Why shouldn't you eat too many sweets? **They usually don't have much of what your body really needs.**

What did we learn?

- Draw a simple food pyramid, including food groups and servings per day. **See www.mypyramid.com for serving suggestions based on a person's age, sex, and activity level.**
- What types of food should you eat the most each day? **Breads and grains.**
- What foods should you eat the least each day? **Sweets and fats.**

TAKING IT FURTHER

- Can a vegetarian eat a balanced diet? Hint: What other foods contain proteins found in meat? **Vegetarians can carefully combine plant products, such as dried beans, legumes, and nuts to obtain the same proteins as in meats.**

- Is it necessary to eat dessert to have a healthy diet? **No, but it depends on what you consider dessert. Pie is not a great choice, but a banana would make a good dessert.**

CHALLENGE: NUTRITION WORKSHEET

- **It is likely that the french fries and hamburger will have more calories, fat, and salt than the other foods. Which food is best for you depends on how you define what is good to eat. Fruits and yogurt are generally lower in calories, fat, and salt, so are probably better for you, but spaghetti with tomato sauce can be very healthy as well.**

LESSON 23

VITAMINS & MINERALS

DO I HAVE TO GO TO A MINE TO GET MINERALS?

SUPPLY LIST

Food in your kitchen   Paper   Pencil

Supplies for Challenge: Research materials on nutrition-related diseases

BEGINNERS

- What are two things you can get from your food that you learned about in this lesson? **Vitamins and minerals.**

- What kind of names are given to vitamins? **Letter names like A, B, and C.**

- How can you make sure you get the vitamins and minerals your body needs? **Eat a variety of healthy foods.**

WHAT DID WE LEARN?

- What are the three main types of compounds found in food? **Carbohydrates, proteins, and fats.**

- How can we be sure to get enough vitamins and minerals in our diet? **The best way is to eat a variety of foods.**

- Why is water so important to our diet? **Our bodies have a lot of water in them and use water for many different functions. Also, we lose water when we sweat and when we breathe, so we need to replace that water every day.**

TAKING IT FURTHER

- Can you drink soda instead of water? **Soda and other drinks have water in them and the body can use that water. However, too much soda or other sweet drinks can give us more calories than we need. Also, soda may have a lot of salt in it, which can be unhealthy if you have too much. Finally, drinks containing sugar or salt can actually make you thirstier!**

- Are frozen dinners just as healthy as fresh food? **Frozen dinners generally have a lot more fat, salt and calories than their fresh-made counterparts. They may be quicker and easier but they are not necessarily healthier.**
- Is restaurant food as healthy as home-cooked food? **It depends on the restaurant. Some restaurants have salad bars and offer lots of choices for healthy foods. However, much restaurant food, especially fast food, is high in fat and calories, and limited in vegetables and fruits.**

CHALLENGE: HEALTH PROBLEMS

- Scurvy: **Lack of vitamin C. Symptoms: tiredness, muscle weakness, joint and muscle aches, spots on the skin, and bleeding gums. Prevention: eat citrus fruits, tomatoes, broccoli, green peppers**
- Rickets: **Lack of vitamin D. Symptoms: softening of the bones leading to skeletal deformity. Prevention: drink milk, eat eggs and fish**
- Anemia: **Lack of iron. Symptoms: Lack of red blood cells causing weakness and fatigue. Prevention: eat meat, eggs, and green leafy vegetables**
- Goiter: **Lack of iodine. Symptoms: Enlarged thyroid gland. Prevention: eat seafood or iodized salt**

QUIZ 4 — DIGESTIVE SYSTEM
LESSONS 19–23

1. Name the six major parts of the digestive system.
   Teeth   Tongue   Esophagus   Stomach   Small intestine   Large intestine

Match the type of tooth with its function.

2. _**B**_ Incisors
3. _**A**_ Canines
4. _**C**_ Bicuspids and Molars

Short answer:

5. Why is it important to take good care of your teeth? **So you don't get cavities or gum disease. To keep your teeth healthy.**
6. How do you take good care of your teeth? **Brush and floss regularly and visit your dentist regularly.**
7. Why is important to eat healthy foods? **To have energy to do the things you want to do and to keep your body healthy.**
8. Name the 5 food groups included in the food pyramid: **Breads/cereals, fruits/vegetables, meats, milk/dairy. (Fats and sweets are not considered a food group.)**
9. Name the three forms of energy in food. **Carbohydrates, proteins, fat** .
10. What two other important types of compounds do we get from our food? **Vitamins and minerals**.

CHALLENGE QUESTIONS

Mark each statement as either True or False.

11. _**T**_ Enzymes play a crucial role in digestion.
12. _**F**_ The gall bladder stores gastric juice.

13. _T_ Pancreatic juice helps break down fats.

14. _T_ Dentine gives the tooth its general size and shape.

15. _F_ Enamel is one of the softest substances in the body.

16. _T_ Orthodontics is the area of dentistry that corrects the alignment of teeth.

17. _T_ A banana has fewer calories than a cup of french fries.

18. _T_ Many diseases can be prevented by eating the right foods.

19. _F_ Rickets can cause bleeding of the gums.

20 _T_ Eating green leafy vegetables can help prevent anemia.

UNIT 5
HEART & LUGS

LESSON 24

THE CIRCULATORY SYSTEM

THE TRANSPORTATION HIGHWAY

SUPPLY LIST

Stopwatch

BEGINNERS

- What is the name of the system that moves your blood around? **Circulatory system.**
- What part of your body pushes the blood around? **The heart.**
- What are two things that the blood takes to all the parts of the body? **Food and oxygen.**
- What is one thing that the blood takes away from the parts of the body? **Carbon dioxide.**

WHAT DID WE LEARN?

- What are the three main parts of the circulatory system? **Heart, blood, and blood vessels.**
- What are two functions of blood? **Supplying food and oxygen and removing waste products.**
- What are three types of blood vessels? **Veins, arteries, and capillaries**.
- Which blood vessels carry blood away from the heart? **Arteries.**
- Which blood vessels carry blood toward the heart? **Veins.**
- What happens to the blood in the capillaries? **Oxygen leaves the red blood cells and enters the surrounding tissue. Then, carbon dioxide enters the red blood cells to be taken to the lungs.**

TAKING IT FURTHER

- How is the circulatory system like a highway? **Red blood cells are like delivery trucks because they carry oxygen, nutrients and carbon dioxide to various parts of the body. Valves are like traffic signals because they keep blood flowing in the right direction. The oxygen, nutrients, and carbon dioxide are the cargo that gets transported. We will learn in later lessons how white blood cells are like policemen and platelets are like a construction crew.**
- Why is exercise important for your circulatory system? **It strengthens your muscles, including your heart.**
- List two other systems that depend on the circulatory system to function properly. **The digestive and respiratory systems both depend heavily on the circulatory system. Actually, every part of your body depends on the circulatory system.**
- Why does your pulse increase when you exercise? **You need more oxygen when you exercise so your heart beats faster to get your blood moving faster, thus giving your body more oxygen.**

HUMAN BODY

LESSON 25

THE HEART

MASTER PUMP

SUPPLY LIST

Copy of "The Heart" worksheet   Blue and red colored pencils

Supplies for Challenge: Cow's heart (beef heart) or sheep's heart (may be fresh or preserved)
Rubber gloves   Sharp knife or scalpel   Anatomy book or dissection guide

BEGINNERS

- What is the part of your body that pumps your blood? **The heart.**
- How was your body designed to protect your heart? **It is in the center of your chest, surrounded by ribs.**
- What can you do to make your heart stronger? **Exercise.**

THE HEART WORKSHEET

A. **To arms and head**   B. **From arms and head**   C. **To lungs**   D. **From lungs**
E. **From legs and lower body**   F. **To legs and lower body**

WHAT DID WE LEARN?

- What are the four chambers of the heart? **Right and left atrium and right and left ventricle.**
- How many times does a blood cell pass through the heart on each trip around the body? **Two times— once before going to the lungs and once when returning from the lungs.**

TAKING IT FURTHER

- What are some things you can do to help your heart stay healthy? **Eat healthy foods, exercise, and don't smoke.**
- Is your heart shaped like a valentine? **No, it is shaped more like a grapefruit about the size of your fist.**
- Does Jesus live in your physical heart? **No. The phrase "ask Jesus into your heart" is not found in the Bible. When a person is saved through repentance and faith, the Spirit of Christ (the Holy Spirit) dwells in his or her heart (Galatians 4:6; Ephesians 3:14–17). However, this "heart" does not refer to the physical organ, but to the "inner man." Jesus cannot live in someone's heart as He is seated at the right hand of the throne of God (Ephesians 1:20; Hebrews 8:1).**

LESSON 26

BLOOD

DELIVERY TRUCKS AND POLICEMEN

SUPPLY LIST

Several chairs   Several children (if available)   Red Hots candies   Corn syrup
Red and blue construction paper   White jelly beans   Candy sprinkles

BEGINNERS

- What is plasma? **The liquid part of blood that blood cells float in.**
- What are the two kinds of blood cells in your blood? **Red and white blood cells.**
- What do platelets do? **Help seal off cuts.**

WHAT DID WE LEARN?

- What are the four parts of blood and the function of each part? **Plasma transports the blood cells; red blood cells carry oxygen, carbon dioxide and nutrients; white blood cells fight germs and other foreign substances; and platelets close wounds.**
- What does your body do to help protect itself if you get cut? **Platelets swarm to the cut and make a patch.**
- Do you have more red or white blood cells? **Many times more red blood cells than white blood cells.**

TAKING IF FURTHER

- What are some of the dangers of a serious cut? **You can lose too much blood or get an infection.**

CHALLENGE: BLOOD TRANSFUSIONS

- If you add the Rh factor to your chart which blood type is the universal donor and which is the universal recipient? **O can donate to all types, A can donate to A and AB, B can donate to B and AB, and AB can only donate to AB.   O can only receive type O, A can receive A or O, B can receive B or O, and AB can receive any type of blood. O is the universal donor, AB is the universal recipient. If you include Rh factor, the universal donor is O negative and the universal recipient is AB positive.**

LESSON 27
THE RESPIRATORY SYSTEM

A BREATH OF FRESH AIR

SUPPLY LIST

Copy of "The Respiratory System" worksheet

BEGINNERS

- What are the major organs that you use when you breathe? **Your lungs.**
- What is the main purpose for breathing? **To get oxygen from the air into your body.**
- What substance leaves your body when you breathe out? **Carbon dioxide.**

THE RESPIRATORY SYSTEM

A. **Nasal cavity**   B. **Throat**   C. **Lung**   D. **Nose**   E. **Alveoli**   F. **Bronchial tube**
G. **Trachea**   H. **Diaphragm**

WHAT DID WE LEARN?

- Describe the breathing process. **Your diaphragm contracts, expanding the chest cavity. Air fills the lungs and gases are exchanged. Then your diaphragm relaxes and the air exits the lungs.**

- How do the circulatory and respiratory systems work together? **The circulatory system moves the blood around the body. In the lungs, the respiratory system exchanges gases with the blood.**

- Where inside the lungs does the exchange of gases occur? **In the capillaries surrounding the alveoli**

- What are the major parts of the respiratory system? **Nose, nasal passage, throat or pharynx, trachea, bronchi, lungs, alveoli, and diaphragm.**

TAKING IT FURTHER

- How do you suppose your body keeps food from going into your lungs and air from going into your stomach when both enter your body in the back of your throat? **You have a flap of tissue that covers the opening to the trachea when you swallow but opens up when you breathe.**

- How does your respiratory system respond when you exercise? **Your brain senses that you need more oxygen when you are exercising, so it instructs your body to take more breaths. So you breathe faster.**

- How does your respiratory system respond when you are sleeping? **Your brain senses that you need less oxygen when you are asleep than when you are awake, so it instructs your body to take slower deeper breaths than when you are awake.**

THE LUNGS

ARE THERE BALLOONS INSIDE MY CHEST?

SUPPLY LIST

Cloth tape measure   1 or more balloons   Stop watch

BEGINNERS

- If you could look inside your lungs would they look like balloons? **No.**
- What is at the end of the tubes inside your lungs? **Tiny air sacs.**
- What is something you can do to keep your lungs healthy? **Exercise and don't smoke.**

WHAT DID WE LEARN?

- How does your body keep harmful particles from entering your lungs? **Hairs in the nasal passage filter particles, tissues in the throat trap and kill bacteria and bronchial tubes are lined with mucous that traps particles.**

- How are your lungs similar to a balloon? **They both get bigger when filled with air and smaller when the air goes out.**

- How are your lungs different from a balloon? **A balloon is an empty sac; lungs have thousands of tiny sacs at the end of a series of branching pipes.**

TAKING IT FURTHER

- What can you do to keep your lungs healthy? **Exercise, try to avoid being around people who are sick if possible, and don't smoke.**

- If you breathe in oxygen and breathe out carbon dioxide, how can you help someone who is not breathing by breathing into his or her lungs when you do CPR? **Air going into the lungs is about 21% oxygen and 0.04% carbon dioxide. Air exiting the lungs is about 16% oxygen and 4% carbon dioxide. So when you breathe into someone else's lungs there is still quite a bit of oxygen in the air you exhale into their lungs.**

HEART & LUNGS

LESSONS 24–28

Fill in the blank with the part of blood that does each job below.

1. _**Red blood cells**_ transport oxygen and carbon dioxide.

2. _**White blood cells**_ surround and eliminate germs.

3. _**Plasma**_ carries the cells around the body.

4. _**Platelets**_ repair breaks in the blood vessels.

Match the term with its definition.

5. _**C**_ Diaphragm

6. _**A**_ Carbon dioxide

7. _**F**_ Oxygen

8. _**B**_ Bronchi

9. _**G**_ Trachea

10. _**D**_ Lungs

11. _**E**_ Alveoli

12. List two ways to keep your lungs healthy: **Exercise, don't smoke, and avoid exposure to people who are ill.**

CHALLENGE QUESTIONS

Short answer:

13. What is the difference between systolic and diastolic blood pressure? **Systolic blood pressure is the pressure in the blood vessels when the heart is contracting, diastolic is the pressure when the heart is resting.**

14. List two ways that a person might lower his/her blood pressure? **Change in diet, exercise, and medication.**

15. Describe how blood moves through the heart. **Blood enters the right atrium then fills the right ventricle. It is then pumped out to the lungs. Blood returning from the lungs enters the left atrium and then fills the left ventricle. It is then pumped out of the heart to the rest of the body.**

16. Which blood type or types can donate to someone with A positive blood? **O positive, A positive, O negative, A negative.**

17. Which blood type or types can someone with A positive blood donate to? **A positive, AB positive.**

18. Explain the difference between external and internal respiration. **External respiration takes place in the lungs, internal respiration takes place between the blood cells and the tissue cells.**

UNIT 6
SKIN & IMMUNITY

LESSON
29

THE SKIN

KEEPING YOUR INSIDES IN

SUPPLY LIST

Hand lotion   Mirror

BEGINNERS

- What kinds of things does your skin keep out of your body? **Dirt, germs, and harmful rays from the sun.**
- What kinds of things does your skin keep inside your body? **All of your organs, blood, and moisture.**
- How does your skin help you control your body temperature? **It allows you to sweat to cool off.**
- How does your skin work together with the nervous system? **It contains nerves that let you feel things.**

WHAT DID WE LEARN?

- What are the purposes of skin? **To protect you from the outside world, to keep your insides in and moist, and to hold the nerves that collect information for your brain.**
- How does skin help you stay healthy? **Primarily, it helps keep out germs.**
- How does skin allow you to move without getting stretched out? **It has elastin; an elastic substance that stretches then returns to its normal shape.**

TAKING IT FURTHER

- Other than skin, in what other ways does your body keep out germs? **Your nose and mouth have mucus and saliva that trap germs. Earwax helps to keep out germs. Hairs in your nose and ears help to keep out foreign objects. Scabs and white blood cells also keep out or get rid of germs.**
- What skin problems might you experience in a dry climate? **Skin can get too dry and crack open, creating painful sores.**
- What skin problems might you experience in a very moist or humid climate? **Your skin might secrete too much oil, causing oily skin. This can lead to acne.**
- What are the dangers of a serious burn? **A serious burn takes away your skin and allows germs in. This can lead to infection and serious illness.**

HUMAN BODY

CROSS-SECTION OF SKIN

WHAT'S BELOW THE SURFACE?

LESSON 30

SUPPLY LIST

Copy of "Skin Word Search"

Supplies for Challenge: Research materials on baldness

BEGINNERS

- How many layers does your skin have? **Three.**
- Which layer of skin keeps water out? **The outermost layer.**
- Which layer of skin has fat cells? **The innermost layer.**
- Which layer of skin contains nerves? **The middle layer.**

SKIN WORD SEARCH

F	**E**	**P**	**I**	**D**	**E**	**R**	**M**	**I**	**S**	S	I	D	O	I
S	K	N	E	D	F	T	**F**	**E**	Q	E	R	D	S	J
A	N	I	O	P	R	T	**A**	**L**	P	**D**	**F**	A	L	G
U	E	**S**	**U**	**B**	**C**	**U**	**T**	**A**	**N**	**E**	**O**	**U**	**S**	D
S	T	**K**	F	R	M	S	E	**S**	W	**R**	**L**	K	J	E
F	O	**I**	L	L	M	N	B	**T**	I	**M**	**L**	O	D	R
P	O	**N**	H	H	**B**	E	R	I	**N**	**I**	**I**	S	E	V
S	E	**K**	**E**	**R**	**A**	**T**	**I**	**N**	**G**	**S**	C	A	S	A
V	**G**	C	X	F	**R**	O	U	U	**E**	S	**L**	F	D	R
Y	**L**	R	I	T	**R**	T	**N**	**E**	**R**	**V**	**E**	**S**	K	R
N	**A**	T	D	G	**I**	B	U	G	**M**	F	K	H	I	L
E	**N**	S	M	I	**E**	L	K	F	**S**	**W**	**E**	**A**	**T**	D
R	**D**	I	W	**P**	**R**	**O**	**T**	**E**	**C**	**T**	**I**	**O**	**N**	G
A	**S**	A	R	E	W	**I**	O	P	Y	M	I	T	T	H
G	F	J	K	Y	T	**L**	L	T	O	I	Y	T	E	F

WHAT DID WE LEARN?

- What are the three layers of skin? **Epidermis, dermis, and subcutaneous tissue.**
- What is the purpose of the sebaceous gland? **To secrete oil to keep the skin soft and flexible.**
- In which layer are most receptors located? **The dermis.**

TAKING IT FURTHER

- Explain what happens to your skin when you pick up a pin. **Nerves detect the size and shape of the pin and send a message to your brain. Your brain sends a message to your fingers to pick it up. As you pick it up your skin stretches and bends to the shape of the pin.**
- How does your skin help regulate your body temperature? **Your skin secretes sweat when you are hot, which cools your body as it evaporates. Also, blood vessels in your skin get wider when you are hot to allow more heat to reach the surface of your skin. When you are cold, the blood vessels get smaller to help keep heat in. Fat cells in the subcutaneous tissue also help to insulate your body from temperature changes around you.**

LESSON 31 · FINGERPRINTS

YOU ARE UNIQUE

SUPPLY LIST

Pencil and paper   Clear tape   Index cards
Supplies for Challenge: Light corn syrup   Red food coloring   Paper   Meter stick
Copy of "Blood Splatter Chart"   Newspaper   White paper   Eyedropper

BEGINNERS

- What are fingerprints? **The patterns formed by the hills and valleys of the skin on the ends of your fingers.**
- What are the three main pictures formed by fingerprints? **Arch, loop, and whorl.**

WHAT DID WE LEARN?

- Where can friction skin be found on your body? **On your hands and feet.**
- When are fingerprints formed? **About 3–4 months before birth.**
- What are the three major groups of fingerprints? **Arch, loop, and whorl.**
- Can you identify identical twins by their fingerprints? **Yes, even identical twins have unique fingerprints.**

TAKING IT FURTHER

- What are some circumstances where fingerprints are used? **They are used to identify suspects in a crime, dead bodies, and lost children.**
- Why do prints only occur on the hands and feet? **These are the only areas where friction skin is needed.**
- Do children's fingerprints match their parents' prints? **No, each person has unique prints that do not match either parent.**

LESSON 32 · THE IMMUNE SYSTEM

KEEPING YOU HEALTHY

SUPPLY LIST

Research materials on allergies, diabetes, and arthritis
Supplies for Challenge: Research materials on vaccines and antibiotics

BEGINNERS

- How does your skin help to keep you from getting sick? **It keeps out most of the germs around you.**
- How does the lymph system help to keep you healthy? **It collects germs from the body tissues and takes them to be destroyed.**
- How do white blood cells help to keep you from getting sick? **They destroy invading germs.**

WHAT DID WE LEARN?

- What are the major parts of the immune system? **Skin, lymph, and circulatory systems.**

- What are the two major types of "germs" that make us sick? **Viruses and bacteria**

- How do tears and mucus help fight germs? **Tears break down bacteria; mucus traps them.**

TAKING IT FURTHER

- Why are a fever and a mosquito bite both indications that your immune system is working? **Your brain raises your body temperature in an effort to kill the germs. Swelling around a mosquito bite shows that antibodies are attacking the invading substance.**

CHALLENGE: HELPING OUR IMMUNE SYSTEM

1. What is a vaccine? **A substance that causes the body to generate antibodies against a particular disease.**

2. How do vaccines work? **A small amount of the disease that has been killed or has been made non-toxic is injected into the patient. The body recognizes the invaders and produces antibodies against that disease, so when live viruses enter the body it is ready to fight.**

3. Who developed the first vaccinations? **Edward Jenner developed the first vaccine using cowpox to stimulate immunity to smallpox in 1776. Louis Pasteur built on this work and developed vaccines for anthrax and rabies in the 1870s and 1880s.**

4. What kind of diseases do vaccinations work against? **There are hundreds of vaccines. Some of the most common are mumps, measles, cholera, yellow fever, typhoid, hepatitis, polio, rabies, and tetanus.**

5. How long do vaccinations last? **The length of the immunity varies depending on the disease and the type of substance used to trigger the immune response. Some vaccines, like influenza (flu) must be administered each year because the viruses change quickly. Others, like tetanus and diphtheria need to be updated about every 10 years.**

1. What are antibiotics? **Chemicals that stop the growth of bacteria, fungi, or other microorganisms.**

2. How were antibiotics discovered? **Penicillin is considered the first antibiotic, discovered somewhat by accident by Alexander Fleming in 1928. Fleming found that bacteria were inhibited in a culture dish containing mold.**

3. What are antibiotics used for? **To treat illnesses caused by bacteria, fungi, or certain single celled organisms.**

4. What are some diseases that are treated with antibiotics? **Strep throat, bacterial pneumonia, various infections, and tuberculosis.**

LESSON 33

GENETICS

WHY YOU LOOK LIKE YOU DO

SUPPLY LIST

Copy of "Genetics Quiz"

Supplies for Challenge: DNA model kit (optional but recommended)

Copy of "DNA Puzzle Pieces" (make additional copies for a longer chain)

BEGINNERS

- Where is the information stored that tells what you will look like? **In the genes in your cells.**
- Where did the information in your genes come from? **Your mother and father.**
- Where did the original information come from for Adam's and Eve's genes? **From God at creation.**

WHAT DID WE LEARN?

- What are genes? **Bits of information contained in each cell that control your physical development and many other things about you.**
- Why do children generally look like their parents? **Because half of the information that determines what a child looks like comes from the biological mother and half comes from the biological father.**

TAKING IT FURTHER

- If parents look very different from each other what will their children look like? **It depends on the dominant genes. Generally, siblings look a lot like each other even if their parents look very different, but they have the potential to look very different. A couple in England had a very interesting family. The mother had very dark skin and the father had very light skin. They had twins and one had very dark skin and one had very light skin. The combinations of our genes make each of us a totally unique individual.**
- In the past evolutionists claimed that man evolved independently in different parts of the world and this is where the races came from. If this were true, how likely would it be that the different races could have children together? **This is very unlikely. God created all humans from one man and woman. More recent genetic testing indicates that all humans share a common ancestor just a few thousand years ago, which supports the teachings of the Bible.**

QUIZ 6

SKIN & IMMUNITY

LESSONS 29–33

Choose the best answer for each question.

1. _B_ Which of the following is not a part of your skin?
2. _D_ Which cells are found on the outermost part of the epidermis?
3. _C_ Where is friction skin found on your body?
4. _A_ Which of the following is not a function of the skin?
5. _D_ Which people have the same fingerprints?
6. _B_ Which organ provides a barrier against disease?
7. _A_ Which of the following are produced by white blood cells?
8. _C_ Which of the following does not help filter germs from your body?
9. _A_ How are physical traits passed on from parent to child?
10. _C_ Which of the following grows from a follicle?

CHALLENGE QUESTIONS

Match the term with its definition.

11. _C_ Arrector pili muscles

12. _E_ Vaccination

13. _B_ Albinism

14. _G_ Double helix

15. _F_ DNA

16. _A_ Carotene

17. _D_ Forensic science

18. _I_ Base pair

19. _K_ Thymine

20. _M_ Cytosine

21. _N_ Gene

22. _O_ Chromosome

23. _H_ Dexoyribose

24. _J_ Adenine

25. _L_ Guanine

26. _P_ Mutation

LESSON 34

BODY POSTER

PUTTING IT ALL TOGETHER

FINAL PROJECT SUPPLY LIST

Newsprint or other large paper   Markers   Scissors   Tape   Anatomy book

WHAT DID WE LEARN?

- Name the eight body systems you have learned about? **Skeletal, muscular, nervous, digestive, circulatory, respiratory, immune, and the skin (integumentary system).**

- How do some of the different systems work together? **The circulatory system works with the respiratory system to bring oxygen to the body. The circulatory system works with the digestive system to bring energy to the whole body. The skin works with the nervous system to detect what is going on around us. The muscular system moves the skeleton. They all work together.**

TAKING IT FURTHER

- What other systems can you think of that are in your body but were not discussed in this book? **Reproductive and excretory systems are a couple that were not covered, as well as the endocrine system. These systems are briefly discussed in the Challenge sections. You can learn more from an anatomy book.**

- How do you see evidence of God the Creator in the design of the human body? **Answers will vary.**

HUMAN BODY

LESSONS 1–34

Choose the best answer for each question.

1. _A_ Which of the following are the three main types of fingerprints?
2. _C_ What kind of skin is on the palms of your hands and bottoms of your feet?
3. _B_ Which are not found in skin?
4. _B_ Which is determined by genetics?
5. _D_ Your hip is which type of joint?
6. _A_ What causes a muscle to contract?
7. _C_ Which is not a part of the nervous system?
8. _B_ What is the main function of the hippocampus in the brain?
9. _C_ Which should you eat sparingly for good health?

Match the name of the system to its function.

10. _D_ Circulatory system
11. _A_ Digestive system
12. _E_ Skin
13. _F_ Nervous system
14. _B_ Muscular system
15. _G_ Respiratory system
16. _C_ Skeletal system

Mark each statement as either True or False.

17. _T_ Long bones produce red blood cells.
18. _F_ Your funny bone is a bone in your arm.
19. _T_ It is important to drink plenty of water every day.
20. _T_ You will get most of the vitamins you need if you eat a variety of foods.
21. _F_ White blood cells stop a cut from bleeding too much.
22. _T_ A human heart has four chambers.
23. _T_ Your lungs are filled with branching tubes that end in alveoli.
24. _F_ Your brain is the largest organ in your body.
25. _F_ A sick person will get better if some of his blood is let out.
26. _T_ Skin contains pain and temperature receptors.

CHALLENGE QUESTIONS

Mark each statement as either True or False.

27. _T_ The endocrine system produces hormones.
28. _F_ The excretory system removes nutrients.
29. _T_ The reproduction system was designed to create new life.

30. _F_ Epithelial tissue moves muscles.

31. _T_ Connective tissue holds the body together.

32. _T_ The skeletal system is divided into axial and appendicular parts.

33. _T_ Only humans have the ability to perform complex reasoning.

34. _F_ Cartilage holds bones in place.

35. _F_ Muscles only move bones.

36. _T_ Reflexes are faster than other nervous system responses.

37. _T_ Dendrites receive input.

38. _F_ The Braille alphabet was developed to allow deaf people to communicate.

39. _F_ Rods and cones allow you to eat ice cream.

40. _F_ The cochlea is part of the middle ear.

41. _T_ Enzymes speed up digestion.

Short answer:

42. Name five bones in your body. **Accept reasonable answers**.

43. Name five muscles in your body. **Accept reasonable answers**.

44. Name four functions of the brain. **Controlling the body, moving the body, thinking, remembering, controlling growth, sight, hearing, smelling, tasting, touching**.

45. List the four major blood types. **A, B, AB, O**.

46. Name two diseases caused by poor nutrition. **Scurvy, rickets, goiter, anemia**.

47. Name the three kinds of respiration. **External, internal, cellular** .

48. Name two purposes of melanin. **Protecting skin from ultraviolet light, protecting eyes from ultraviolet light, giving color to eyes, skin, and hair**.

LESSON

34

CONCLUSION

APPRECIATING THE HUMAN BODY

SUPPLY LIST

Bible   Paper   Pencil

APPENDICES

APPENDICES

RESOURCE GUIDE

Many of the following titles are available from Answers in Genesis (www.AnswersBookstore.com).

THE WORLD OF PLANTS

Suggested Books

Trees of North America by C. Frank Brockman—Great guide for tree identification

Reader's Digest North American Wildlife—A great resource to have for any field trip!

The Science of Plants by Jonathan Bocknek—Overview of plants, activities, puzzles for all ages

Plants by Janice VanCleave—Lots of fun activities; science fair ideas

Biology for Every Kid by Janice VanCleave—More fun activities

The Nature and Science of Seeds by Jane Burton and Kim Taylor—Great pictures, overview of less common seeds

Photosynthesis by Alvin Silverstein—In-depth look at the process for upper elementary

How Leaves Change by Sylvia A. Johnson—Great pictures of fall colors, more in-depth information for upper elementary students

God Created the Plants and Trees of the World by Earl & Bonita Snellenberger—Coloring and sticker book for children that teaches about plants and trees from a biblical perspective

Suggested Videos

Newton's Workshop by Moody Institute—Excellent Christian science series; several titles to choose from

Field Trip Ideas
- Creation Museum in Petersburg, KY
- Botanic gardens
- Tour a local nursery, greenhouse, or florist
- Arboretum
- Take a nature walk

THE WORLD OF ANIMALS

Suggested Books

Breathtaking Birds by Buddy and Kay Davis—Animal encyclopedia from a creation perspective

Magnificent Mammals by Buddy and Kay Davis—Animal encyclopedia from a creation perspective

Sensational Sea Creatures by Buddy and Kay Davis—Animal encyclopedia from a creation perspective

Reader's Digest North American Wildlife—A great resource to have for any field trip

Mammals Scholastic Voyages of Discovery by Scholastic Books—Interactive fun

Birds by Carolyn Boulton—Lots of suggested activities, good pictures

Play and Find Out About Bugs by Janice VanCleave—Great experiments

Jellyfish by Leighton Taylor—Good explanation of life cycle, great pictures

Zoo Guide by Answers in Genesis—A guide to over 100 animals from a creationist perspective

Aquarium Guide by Answers in Genesis—Take it to the aquarium with you

Museum Guide by Answers in Genesis—Take it to the natural history museum with you

God Created Series by Earl and Bonita Snellenberger—Coloring and sticker books that present God's creation to young children

Suggested Videos

Newton's Workshop by Moody Institute—Excellent Christian science series

Incredible Creatures that Defy Evolution Three volumes by Exploration Films—Learn about amazing design features

Exploring the Wildlife Kingdom by Exploration Films—Evolution free nature videos

Life's Story by NPN Videos—Shows how the interactions among living things could not have happened through evolution

We highly recommend purchasing one or more of the following to supplement the activities in this book:

Owl pellets
Frog habitat
Butterfly habitat
Dissection supplies

Field Trip Ideas

* Creation Museum in Petersburg, KY
* Farm or dairy
* Zoo, aquarium, or butterfly museum
* Fish hatchery
* Wildlife area

THE HUMAN BODY

Suggested Books

Human Anatomy in Full Color from Dover Publications—Highly recommended

Human Anatomy Coloring Book from Dover—Detailed coloring pages

Biology for Every Kid by Janice VanCleave—Many fun activities

Understanding Your Senses by Rebecca Treays—Good pictures and explanations

Body by Design by Dr. Alan Gillen—Basic anatomy and physiology from a creationist viewpoint

God Created the People of the World by Earl and Bonita Snellenberger—An information-packed coloring and sticker book with the biblical history of people and people groups

Suggested Videos

Newton's Workshop by Moody Institute—Excellent Christian science series

The Hearing Ear and the Seeing Eye by Dr. David Menton—Amazing features God created

Fearfully and Wonderfully Made by Dr. David Menton—Discusses the miracle of birth

Field Trip Ideas

* Creation Museum in Petersburg, Kentucky
* Hospital
* Science museum with human body exhibits
* Doctor's Office

Other Ideas

Build a model of the human body. Inexpensive kits are available from the suppliers listed above.

Dissect a sheep's or cow's heart, brain, or eye. Examining animal parts can give a more realistic idea of what is inside the human body.

CREATION SCIENCE RESOURCES

Answers Book for Kids Four volumes by Ken Ham with Cindy Malott—Answers children's frequently asked questions

The New Answers Book 1 & 2 by Ken Ham and others—Answers frequently asked questions

Dinosaurs by Design by Duane T. Gish—All about dinosaurs and where they fit into creation

The Amazing Story of Creation by Duane T. Gish—Scientific evidence for the creation story

Creation Science by Felice Gerwitz and Jill Whitlock—Unit study focusing on creation

Creation: Facts of Life by Gary Parker—In-depth comparison of the evidence for creation and evolution

Dinosaurs of Eden by Ken Ham—Learn the true history of the earth from the Garden of Eden to the Tower of Babel

Master Supply List

The following table lists all the supplies used for *God's Design for Life* activities. You will need to look up the individual lessons in the student book to obtain the specific details for the individual activities (such as quantity, color, etc.). The letter *c* denotes that the lesson number refers to the challenge activity. Common supplies such as colored pencils, construction paper, markers, scissors, tape, etc., are not listed.

Supplies needed (see lessons for details)	Plants	Animals	Human Body
3-ring binder		2	
Aloe plant	17c		
Aluminum foil			20
Anatomy book			5–34
Balloons		21c, 27c	1, 28
Bible		35	1, 35
Bird feeder (optional)		8	
Bread slices (homemade or with no preservatives)	34		
Butterfly larvae (caterpillars)		23	
Cactus plant	29		
Candy sprinkles			26
Cardboard boxes or shoe boxes	4, 16, 26		
Chicken bones			6c
Chocolate chips (mini size)		29	
Cinnamon, peppermint, and other spices			18
Cocoa (unsweetened)			18
Coffee filters	19c		
Coffee stirrer	27		
Corn meal or yellow sand	21, 31		
Craft sticks	6c		
Dental floss			21
Dissection kit		29c	25c
Dividers with tabs (12 or 13 per student)		2	
DNA model kit (optional)			33c
Dried moss (from craft store)	32		
Encyclopedia (animal)		all	
Encyclopedia (plant and animal)	3		
Eyedropper			31c
Face paint		18	
Fake fur or felt		7	
Fern frond	31		

Supplies needed (see lessons for details)	Plants	Animals	Human Body
Feather (can purchase at craft store)		9	
Field guide (birds)		8	
Field guide (flowers)	5		
Field guide (plants)	27		
Field guide (sea shells)		27	
Field guide (trees)	20		
Fingernail polish remover	19c		
Flexible wire		24	
Flour		21c	
Flower (composite, such as daisy, sunflower, or zinnia—fresh)	23c		
Flower (such as lily—fresh)	23		
Flower bulbs (tulips, daffodils, etc.—optional)	12		
Food coloring	13, 18		31c
Fruits, nuts, and vegetables	4c, 12, 10, 11, 13, 24, 30, 34c		18
Gel pens (washable)			5
Gelatin mix (yellow)	4		
Gloves (rubber or latex)			25c
Goldfish snack crackers		11	
Grass plant	6		
Grapes (red and green)	4		
Gummy worms		31	
Hair/fur from 2 or more mammals		3	
Hairspray (aerosol)	34c		
Hand lotion			29
Heart (from a cow or sheep)			25c
Hydras (live)		28c	
Index cards	7, 17, 20, 34c	22	13, 31
Jars (1 must have a lid)	8, 9, 30		
Jelly beans (white)			26
Knife or scalpel (very sharp)	9, 18, 23, 24		25c
Leaves (fresh)	19c, 20		
Lemon juice			18
Light corn syrup			26, 31c
Magnifying glass	6, 9, 11, 20, 22c, 29, 32	9, 24, 25	8c
Marshmallows (large and small)		24, 28	
Microscope and slides	4c, 22c, 33c	32	
Mirror			1, 21, 29
Modeling clay	21	13, 25, 26c 28	12, 20

Supplies needed (see lessons for details)	Plants	Animals	Human Body
Newspaper		21c	
Newsprint (or other large roll of paper)			34
Owl pellet (optional)		10	
Paper fasteners (brads)			2, 4
Peat moss	32c		
Photo album with magnetic pages or 3-ring binder	20		
Pinecones (scales tightly shut)	10		
Pipe cleaners	21	22, 24, 26c	
Plants (fast-growing; e.g., mint plants)	16, 28		
Plaster of Paris			20
Plastic cups (clear)	13, 32c		
Plastic zipper bags	4, 20, 34	7	15
Pollen	22c		
Pond water	33c	32	
Poster board/tag board	2, 12c, 19, 35	7, 29	20
Potting soil	6c, 13, 30		
Rubber/plastic gloves		29c	25c
Sand dollar (dead and dried; check at craft store—optional)		29	
Spider web (optional)		24	
Starfish (dead and dried; check at craft store—optional)		29	
Red Hots candies			26
Rubber bands			7c
Ruler			11
Salt dough		29	
Scarves		23	
Seeds (bean, corn, grass, coconut, radish)	6c, 8, 9, 10c, 11c		
Sequins or flat beads		16	
Sea shells		27	
Sleeping bag		23	
Soap (anti-bacterial hand)		33	
Sponge (natural—optional)		30	
Sponge (synthetic)		30	
Starfish (preserved for dissection)		29c	
Steak (or other meat—raw)			8c
Steel wool	8		
Stopwatch		6	9, 11, 24, 28
Straight pins			15
Straws (flexible)	21, 27		

Supplies needed (see lessons for details)	Plants	Animals	Human Body
String		21c	
Styrofoam balls		22	
Swabs			18
Tacks			7c
Tadpoles and tank (optional)		15	
Tape (cloth)		19	
Tape measure (cloth—the kind used for sewing)			28
Tape measure (metal)			4c
Tempera paints		30	
Toothbrush		6	21
Toothpaste			21
Toothpicks		22, 24	14
Vinegar			6c, 18
Wooden pencils			7c
Yard stick/meter stick			9, 31c
Yarn		32	

WORKS CITED

WORLD OF PLANTS

Adams, A. B. *Eternal Quest: The Story of the Great Naturalists*. New York: G.P. Putnam's Sons, 1969.

Bocknek, Jonathan. *The Science of Plants*. Milwaukee: Gareth Stevens Publishing, 1999.

Brockman, C. Frank. *Trees of North America*. New York: Golden Press, 1968.

Burnie, David. *Eyewitness Books Plants*. New York: Alfred A. Knopf, 1989.

Burton, Jane, and Kim Taylor. *The Nature & Science of Seeds*. Milwaukee: Gareth Stevens Publishing, 1999.

"Cobra Lily." http://www.bugbitingplants.com/cobra_lily.php.

Challand, Helwn J. *Plants Without Seeds*. Chicago: Children's Press, 1986.

"A Concise History of the Rose—The King of Flowers." http://www.indiainternational.com.

Croll, Carolyn. *Redoute The Man Who Painted Flowers*. New York: G. P. Putnam's Sons, 1996.

'Espinasse, M. *Robert Hooke*. Berkeley: University of California Press, 1962.

Evans, Erv and Blazich, Frank. *Overcoming Seed Dormancy: Trees and Shrubs*. http://www.ces.ncsu.edu/depts/hort/hil/hil-8704.html.

"The Faces of Science: African Americans in the Sciences." http://webfiles.uci.edu/mcbrown/display/faces.html.

Giannotti, Heike. *The History of Rose Culture in France*. University of Illinois, 2001.

Giesecke, Ernestine. *Outside My Window Flowers*. Des Plaines: Heinemann Library, 1999.

Gish, Duane T. *The Amazing Story of Creation from Science and the Bible*. El Cajon: Institute for Creation Research, 1990.

Gish, Duane T. *Dinosaurs by Design*. Colorado Springs: Creation Life Publishers, 1992.

Greenaway, Theresa. *Mosses & Liverworts*. Austin: Steck-Vaughn Co., 1992.

Greenaway, Theresa. *The Plant Kingdom*. Austin: Steck-Vaughn Co., 2000.

Ham, Ken et al. *The Answers Book*. El Cajon: Master Books, 1992.

Jebens, Brandon. *The Biogeography of Sequoia Sempervirens*. San Fancisco: San Francisco State University, 1999.

Johnson, Sylvia A. *How Leaves Change*. Minneapolis: Lerner Publications Co., 1986.

Karaler, Lucy. *Green Magic Algae Rediscovered*. New York: Thomas Y. Crowell, 1983.

Koerner, L. *Linnaeus: Nature and Nation*. Cambridge: Harvard University Press, 1999.

Lindroth, S. *The Two Faces of Linnaeus*. Berkeley: University of California Press, 1983.

Moore, J. A. *Science as a Way of Knowing*. Cambridge: Harvard University Press, 1993.

Morris, John D., Ph.D. *The Young Earth*. Colorado Springs: Master Books, 1994.

Parker, Gregory, and others. *Biology: God's Living Creation*. 2nd ed. Pensacola: A Beka Book, 1986.

Omahen, Sharen, *Seed Storage Facility is Modern Day Noah's Ark*. http://www.uga.edu/discover/educators/readings/read187.pdf, April, 2003.

"Pierre-Joseph Redoute." http://www.globalgallery.com/bios/redoute.

Reader's Digest. *North American Wildlife*. Pleasantville: Reader's Digest Association, 1982.

Rogers, Kirsteen et al. *Usborne Science Encyclopdia*. London: Usborne Publishing, 2002.

Rudwick, M. J. S. *The Meaning of Fossils*. Chicago: University of Chicago Press, 1985.

Schiebinger, L. "The Loves of Plants." *Scientific American*. February 1996: 110-115.

Selsam, Millicent E. *Mushrooms*. New York: William Morrow & Co., 1986.

Silverstein, Alvin, and others. *Photosynthesis*. Brookfield: Twenty-first Century Books, 1998.

Steele, DeWitt. *Investigating God's World*. Pensacola: A Beka Book Publications, 1986.

"This Person in Black History 4: George Washington Carver." http://sps.k12.mo.us/historyday/feb/carver.htm.

"The Truly Amazing Redwood Tree." http://www.treesofmystery.net/sequoia.htm.

VanCleave, Janice. *Biology for Every Kid*. New York: John Wiley & Sons, Inc., 1990.

VanCleave, Janice. *Plants*. New York: John Wiley & Sons, Inc., 1997.

Wexler, Jerome. *From Spore to Spore*. New York: Dodd, Mead & Co., 1985.

WORLD OF ANIMALS

Adams, A. B. *Eternal Quest: The Story of the Great Naturalists*. New York: G.P. Putnam's Sons, 1969.

Bargar, Sherie, and Linda Johnson. *Rattlesnakes*. Vero Beach: Rourke Enterprises, Inc., 1986.

"Birds." http://www.earthlife.net/birds.

Cardwardine, Mark, et.al. *Whales, Dolphins & Porpoises*. Sydney: US Weldon Owen Inc., 1998.

Chinery, Michael. *Butterfly*. Mahwah: Troll Associates, 1991.

Chinery, Michael. *Shark*. Mahwah: Troll Associates, 1991.

Coldrey, Jennifer. *Shells*. New York: Dorling Kindersley, Inc., 1993.

Cole, Joanna. *A Bird's Body*. New York: William Morrow & Co., 1982.

Cousteau Society. *Corals: The Sea's Great Builders*. New York: Simon & Shuster, 1992.

'Espinasse, M. *Robert Hooke*. Berkeley: University of California, 1962.

Evans, J. Edward. *Charles Darwin Revolutionary Biologist*. Minneapolis: Lerner Publications, 1993.

Fleisher, Paul. *Gorillas*. New York: Benchmark Books, 2001.

Gish, Duane T., Ph.D. *The Amazing Story of Creation*. El Cajon: Institute for Creation Research, 1990.

"Georges Cuvier." http://www.ucmp.berkeley.edu/history/cuvier.

Gowell, Elizabeth Tayntor. *Whales and Dolphins What They Have in Common*. New York: Franklin Watts, 1999.

Ham, Ken. *The Great Dinosaur Mystery Solved!* Green Forest: Master Books, 1999.

Hird, Ed. "Dr. Louis Pasteur: Servant of All." *Deep Cove Crier*. December 1997.

Jackson, Tom. *Nature's Children Rattlesnakes*. Danbury: Grolier Educational, 2001.

Kalman, Bobbie, and Allison Larin. *What is a Fish?* New York: Crabtree Publishers, 1999.

Koerner, L. *Linnaeus: Nature and Nation*. Cambridge: Harvard University, 1999.

Lacey, Elizabeth A. *The Complete Frog a Guide for the Very Young Naturalist*. New York: Lothrop, Lee & Shepard Books, 1989.

Landau, Elaine. *Sea Horses*. New York: Children's Press, 1999.

Lindroth, S. *The Two Faces of Linnaeus*. Berkeley: University of California Press, 1983.

"Louis Pasteur." http://web.ukonline.co.uk/b.gardner/pasteur.htm.

Maynard, Thane. *Primates Apes, Monkeys, Prosimians*. New York: Franklin Watts, 1994.

Markle, Sandra. *Outside and Inside Kangaroos*. New York: Atheneum Books for Young Readers, 1999.

Moore, J. A. *Science as a Way of Knowing*. Cambridge: Harvard University Press, 1993.

Morris, John D., Ph.D. *The Young Earth*. Colorado Springs: Master Books, 1994.

National Geographic Book of Mammals. Washington, D.C.: National Geographic Society, 1998.

Parker, Gregory et al. *Biology: God's Living Creation*. Pensacola: A Beka Books, 1997.

Parker, Steve. *Charles Darwin and Evolution*. London: HarperCollins Publishers, 1992.

Ross, Michael E. *Wormology*. Minneapolis: Carolrhoda Books, Inc., 1996.

Rudwick, M.J. S. *The Meaning of Fossils*. Chicago: University of Chicago Press, 1985.

Scholastic Voyages of Discovery Mammals. New York: Scholastic, Inc., 1997.

Stone, Lynn M. *Tasmanian Devil*. Vero Beach: Rourke Corptoration, Inc., 1990.

Swan, Erin Pembrey. *Meat-eating Marsupials*. New York: Franklin Watts, 2002.

Swan, Erin Pembrey. *Primates: From Howler Monkeys to Humans*. New York: Franklin Watts, 1998.

Taylor, Leighton. *Jellyfish*. Minneapolis: Lerner Publishing Co., 1998.

VanCleave, Janice. *Biology for Every Kid*. New York: John Wiley & Sons, Inc., 1990.

VanCleave, Janice. *Insects and Spiders*. New York: John Wiley & Sons, Inc., 1998.

VanCleave, Janice. *Play and Find Out About Bugs*. New York: John Wiley & Sons, Inc., 1999.

Walters, Martin. *The Simon & Schuster Young Readers' Book of Animals*. New York: Simon & Schuster, Inc., 1990.

HUMAN BODY

"A ,B, Cs of Brain Tumors." http://www.brain-surgery.com/primer.html.

Adams, A. B. *Eternal Quest: The Story of the Great Naturalists*. New York: G.P. Putnam's Sons, 1969.

Collins, David R. *God's Servant at the Battlefield Florence Nightingale*. Milford: Mott Media, 1985.

'Espinasse, M. *Robert Hooke*. Berkeley: University of California Press, 1962.

"Florence Nightingale." http://www.countryjoe.com/nightingale.

Gish, Duane T., Ph.D. *The Amazing Story of Creation From Science and the Bible*. El Cajon: Institute for Creation Research, 1990.

Gish, Duane T., Ph.D. *Dionsaours by Design*. Colorado Springs: Creation-Life Publishers, 1992.

"Gregor Mendel." http://www.accessexcellence.org.

Ham, Ken et al. *The Answers Book*. El Cajon: Master Books, 1992.

Harcup, John W. *Human Anatomy in Full Color*. Mineola: Dover Publications, Inc., 1996.

"How the Immune System Works." http://health.howstuffworks.com/immune-system.htm.

Jefferies, David. *The Human Body*. Huntington Beach: Teacher Created Materials, Inc., 1993.

Koerner, L. *Linnaeus: Nature and Nation*. Cambridge: Harvard University Press, 1999.

Lindroth, S. *The Two Faces of Linnaeus*. Berkeley: University of California Press, 1983.

Mangiardi, John R., and Howard Kane. *History of Brain Surgery*. www.brain-surgery.com.

"Mapping the Motor Cortex." http://www.pbs.org/wgbh/aso/tryit/brain/cortexhistory.html.

Moore, J. A. *Science as a Way of Knowing*. Cambridge: Harvard University Press, 1993.

Morris, John D. *The Young Earth*. Colorado Springs: Master Books, 1994.

Parker, Gregory, and others. *Biology God's Living Creation*. Pensacola: A Beka Books, 1997.

Roehm, Michelle. *Girls Who Rocked the World*. Hillsboro: Beyond Words Publishing, 2000.

Rudwick, M.J. S. *The Meaning of Fossils*. Chicago: University of Chicago Press, 1985.

Schiebinger, L. "The Loves of the Plants." *Scientific American*. February 1996: 110–115.

Steele, DeWitt. *Investigating God's World*. Pensacola: A Beka Books, 1986.

Treays, Rebecca. *Understanding Your Senses*. London: Usborne Publishing, Ltd., 1997.

VanCleave, Janice. *Biology for Every Kid*. New York: John Wiley & Sons, 1990.

VanCleave, Janice. *Plants*. New York: John Wiley & Sons, 1990.

VanderMeer, Ron, and Ad Dudnik. *The Brain Pack*. Datchet: VanderMeer Publishing, 1996.